AMERICA
THROUGH THE EYE
OF MY NEEDLE

AMERICA
THROUGH THE EYE
OF MY NEEDLE

COMMON SENSE FOR THE '80s

JOSEPHINE ALEXANDER

THE DIAL PRESS
NEW YORK

Published by
The Dial Press
1 Dag Hammarskjold Plaza
New York, New York 10017

Manufactured in the United States of America

First printing

Design by Karin Batten

Library of Congress Cataloging in Publication Data

Alexander, Josephine.
  America through the eye of my needle.

  Includes bibliographical references.
    1. United States—Economic conditions—1971–
2. United States—Social conditions—1960–
I. Title.
HC106.7.A365   330.973'0926   80-18928
ISBN 0-8037-0194-2

To my granddaughters,
Jody and Katy

CONTENTS

INTRODUCTION:

SEARCHING FOR THE NEEDLE IN AMERICA'S HAYSTACK

When this century and I were young, the American Dream joined us for dinner every evening. My father was its standard bearer. He had been a school dropout at twelve to help his mother support his ailing father and the brood of little sisters and baby brother. By the time I sat by his side in my highchair in New Orleans, he was vice-president and general manager of one of the South's biggest molasses refineries and canneries.

Our circle of friends, relatives, and business associates belonged in one degree or another to the free-enterprise system, either through personal success like my father's or by inherited interest.

The second decade of the century was a time of free enterprise. The country's handful of great monopoly fortunes—those of the Rockefellers, Morgans, Schwabs—were centered far away in the Northeast or Midwest, and my father's hero, Teddy Roosevelt, was making a great noise about busting up un-American trusts.

The first grown-up conversations I heard were of American know-how. Those success stories seem so moderate now—tales of mere millionaires with just a factory or two or a bank or two to their names.

As for politics, my father boasted that even though he lived in the solidly Democratic South his vote did not slavishly follow party lines. No, sir. He always voted for the best man. By "best man" he meant the most articulate upholder of hard work, ambition, American know-how, and success.

My Uncle Joe, my mother's brother for whom I had been optimistically named, was even more successful than my father. But then, he had a more privileged start. His father was rabbi of Vicksburg, Mississippi, and a modestly successful writer, and had been able to send him north for a legal education. Joe had then taken Horace Greeley's advice and gone west, to prosper in San Francisco.

By 1914, the year of the Panama Pacific Exposition, Uncle Joe could afford to treat my family to a summer vacation in San Francisco, where his wonderful status symbol, an automobile, was even more magical than the glowing, fairyland exposition. In a few more years, Uncle Joe had a country home on the hilltop of a ten-acre orchard in the San Francisco peninsula, and our five-day train trips to the Coast as soon as school ended became annual affairs. By 1928, Uncle Joe had amassed a million dollars in stocks and bonds.

Meantime, I was storing up firsthand train-travel knowledge of my country before, during, and shortly after World War I. Through train windows I saw the lush and beautiful South, with its cane fields and cypress swamps, and those curiosity-rousing shanties and shanty towns scattered along the train tracks. Occasionally, our trips took us through the Midwest, where we visited family and friends in Minnesota and Illinois, but more often we traveled the Southwest route. This was still frontier country, vast undeveloped rangeland scattered with stock farms, scurries of wild creatures, spots of green farmland, and country towns—exciting and romantic to my lively young imagination. Once in a while a car or truck could be sighted as a cloud of dust far off through the crystal air.

More crystal still was the air around my uncle's hilltop, for some of the roads in California were actually paved, so the infrequent cars and trucks traveled without raising dust.

During the summer there would be adventurous drives in my uncle's touring car and occasional jaunts to San Francisco to spend a few days at a hotel, visiting cousins, shopping, and going to the theaters and museums. Our drives would be through family orchards, truck farms, dairy and poultry farms, and modest roadside businesses that served the moderate highway traffic.

The drives were fun, but I liked it better yet when we went by train. Train travel was our soap opera: on trains we might silently observe exciting vignettes of mystery and romance, or engage in snatches of conversation with people from other worlds. And at the end of the line was the bustle of San Francisco's Third and Townsend Station, through which the great and the shabby bustled from every part of the world, hurrying about their mysterious business.

I think I was thirteen when I first learned that the free-enterprise system did not always run on an even keel but had cycles of boom and bust. Excited by World War I prosperity, my father had overexpanded, and when the postwar recession hit he had to sell his factory to a competitor. He was left with a small amount of capital to make a middle-aged second start, but his self-confidence held firm and he decided to take us to San Francisco for good.

Once settled, he soon went to work Horatio-Algering it to ownership of a small, choice furniture factory. Meantime, my Uncle Joe staked his namesake, me, to tuition in one of the most exclusive private schools in the city.

Today, the families of my schoolmates would mostly be classed as "poor-rich."* Then they were among the city's social

* An article by Bob Greene in the *San Francisco Chronicle* of July 16, 1979, noted that there were more than 240,000 persons with net assets of $1 million or more in 1976, according to *U.S. News and World Report.* Economists predicted that this figure would reach 250,000 by the end of 1978. Of the estimated 250,000, "150,000 are strivers who merely acquired a little capital recently and who will have to be considered just poor rich unless their fortunes climb drastically. . . . Only the last 25,000 with minimum assets of $200 million are entitled to be called really-really rich. . . . At the top of the heap are the Rockefellers, Fords, Hunts, Ahmasons, du Ponts, Phippses, Dorrances, Pews, and Motts, just a few of the capitalist families in America whose combined wealth equals all the other small change left in the world." ("The Rich Are Different: Why the Wealthy Have More Fun," p. 15)

leaders. Most of the fathers owned and operated their own un-diversified factories, shops, or financial institutions.

After graduation, my uncle's bounty allowed me to go on to the university, traveling each week from San Francisco to Berkeley by trolley car, ferryboat, and electric train. In those days, precious few of even my most prosperous friends and fellow students owned cars. For those who did, weekend trips to country home or coast, and drives into the rolling, hilly farmland so near the campus, were delightful. But the wish for a car had no urgency for the rest of us. Trolleys, railroads, fer-ryboats, riverboats, and jitneys beckoned in every direction, promising lively, friendly, companionable excursions. And we took frequent walks at any time of the day or night, because then we could walk without fear.

The stock-market crash of 1929 occurred when I was about midway to graduation. My Uncle Joe did not jump from his of-fice window, as some of his friends did, but he was not a millionaire anymore, and one of his necessary retrenchments was his allowance to me. I was able to get a student loan, add a quick course in shorthand and typing to my college schedule, and finish college by working part-time at a secretarial job that led to a full-time university position after graduation.

The Great Depression was taking its toll all about me, but the suddenly deflated dollar bought so much that anyone like me, who could earn a small steady income, did fine.

My Depression problems were serious, but they were not fi-nancial. They stemmed from the two-way pull between my conservative family, who insisted that the quarter of our popu-lation without jobs was just not looking hard enough or was too proud to start at the bottom as my father had done, and my soon-radicalized friends and classmates who thought the free-enterprise system was bankrupt. They argued that we should follow the Soviets' lead because Russia was the only country without massive unemployment, and most of the rest of our world was whirling toward fascism, Nazism, anti-Semitism, and war.

There I was, a middle-of-the-roader caught in a tight squeeze. While my family and their circle berated FDR as a wild-eyed radical, while my friends and a few of my professors branded him the bulwark of an outworn system, I pinned my hopes on the second President Roosevelt, the New Dealer, whose pump priming would bolster the American Dream and end the Depression—just as my father had pinned his on the first President Roosevelt, the Great Trust Buster.

I did just what thirty years later, I was to watch hundreds of thousands of my young fellow citizens do in their efforts to cope with the different problems of the sixties. I ran away. I tried to turn my personal time clock back a generation or two. First, I went for a brief vacation to that vast, arid frontier land I had known from the train window. Then I married an Arizona homesteader whose impoverished dairy ranch was plunked right in the middle of it.

So, during the last years of the Great Depression, the buildup to World War II that ended it, the war years that brought prosperity—for thirteen years of my adult life—I learned how our pioneer ancestors had lived: by hard work, with little and sometimes no money, but sustained by proud self-sufficiency and golden dreams of the future we were building for our children and our country. We had few modern conveniences—no electricity, telephone, or decent roads—but my husband and I managed to borrow five hundred dollars and build a good-sized adobe house which we planned to stock with children as soon as we could afford them.

One item we did not need for our house was a lock. People in the country left doors unlocked, and I did not find this custom strange. During my last year in Berkeley I had rented a fifteen-dollar-a-month apartment that was much too pleasant, with its sunny porch and garden and charming view, not to share with less fortunate friends, so I would invite them to drop by, and leave the door unlocked when I went to work.

My husband and I did not wait to finish the house before we began planting lots of trees and shrubs. We were founding a dynasty, sinking deep roots for ourselves, the children we hoped for, and the generations to come. Soon we cleared more land and drilled a big, deep irrigation well.

When America joined the war, the army rejected my husband as physically unfit for cannon fodder, but the president urged us all to raise food to win the peace, so the two of us leaped to the breach: we produced beef, pork, honey, grain, poultry, eggs, and acres of produce. And we finally had two children.

For thirteen years and some months, then, I extended my view and understanding of our American Dream backward into the past, and added a lot more firsthand knowledge of the present than I had bargained for. By 1948, I was ready to rejoin my own century and my rightful place in our nation's time zone, and I took the two children and returned—I thought—to the place, the era, I had left behind me.

Hah! I was Mrs. Rip Van Winkle! The job old Rip had in adjusting to his world was child's play compared to mine when I returned to the San Francisco Bay area after my thirteen-year dropout. Inflation, unemployment from an oncoming postwar recession, inadequate child-care centers and these with long waiting lists (a woman's place was in the home, don't you know), new kinds of cities, new kinds of transportation or lack thereof; a new kind of air, thick with noise pollution—all these were the beginnings of a different but as yet unrecognized new economic and social structure.

My old friends, relatives, and succession of new neighbors had been part of the gradual changes that I had missed, and had adapted to them as well as they could, bit by bit. I had returned, still with the image of the time so shortly passed, so contrasts came at me from every direction. The most jolting change was the sense of impermanence I felt at every hand. When I had left, the structures of families and social circles had been fairly stable; I returned to find nuclear families torn loose from their roots. People drifted from city to suburb to countryside, to small town and back to city, oppressed by the physical and social problems in each locale—housing shortages, inflation, congestion, and the stress created by constantly increasing traffic that took its toll in time, money, energy, and too often life. In my innocence I had thought I was returning from isolation to community, but I found what was later aptly called a lonely crowd.

When I came back from the frontier to the modern metropolis, I had seen no need for the luxury of a car in my unluxurious budget. I thought I would return to the cheap, frequent, fast public transportation I knew so well. But I soon learned that though I could not afford a car, I had to have one: without my own car I could find no solutions to my many problems: affordable housing, child care, job hunting, all the chores of making do on a tight budget. A car I had to have, and I'd have to learn to cope with the new kind of traffic I had not dealt with before: congested, hazardous, and damnably slow.

With soaring inflation and meager job opportunities I could not buy a house—and landlords hated children, even nondestructive ones like mine. So we turned into tumbleweed, blowing from city to suburb to country, from East Bay to North Bay, from farmstead tenantry to middle-sized city, and finally in the mid-fifties we lighted in a coastal fishing village, Bodega Bay. An asthmatic child needed clean air. Wherever we lived, we needed a car, so I needed two jobs to support the four of us: three with legs and one with wheels. I finished the fifties working full time as a secretary-librarian and on my own even fuller time as a "stringer," a self-employed journalist and photographer.

Meanwhile, wherever I lived, but especially in the cities, I found growing threats on every hand. I saw anger on the faces of people who had torn themselves out of their families and communities to come to work in war-created jobs, and then found themselves beached in shoddy, segregated, wartime housing, frustrated in their efforts to find postwar jobs in a shrinking market. These rootless people were often subjected to brutalizing police bigotry and violence—and they had nothing to go back home to.

Disorientation was seeping into all strata, rich and poor.

People were growing disillusioned with work that, whatever the material rewards, was a mockery of free enterprise.

In the cities, as the postwar population exploded, the differences in the problems of blacks and whites were differences in *degree*, not kind—the lack of jobs, housing, decent schools. Blacks and whites endured the same stresses, tensions, lashing out at neighbors and family over often petty frustrations. They were driven by their grim memories of the Depression. All around me people were going after dollars that melted in their hands. On the rooftops, even in poor, drab neighborhoods, a forest of television antennas was springing up, and the air was vibrant with the hypnotic barking of an unending electronic carnival.

One day I drove my children down the San Francisco peninsula to show them the hilltop orchard where I used to spend my summer vacations. Gone were the family farms, dairies, roadside businesses. In their place were freeways filled with bumper-to-bumper traffic. A yellow-brown haze over the landscape obscured the hills, and the constant roar of planes thundered overhead. In what was now called Silicon Valley, site of much of our ever-expanding electronics and war industries, the hills and valleys still looked contour ploughed, but now they were planted, not with trees and produce but with houses, uniform, boxlike, impermanent-looking, and shopping centers in endless fields. It was the great slurb to which families and industry, fleeing from the decaying cities, had swarmed, seeking their dream vision of open space, security, and tranquillity.

My uncle's orchard was gone, but the charmingly remodeled old farmhouse still crested the hill. There were still some oases of verdure and privacy for the especially well-to-do of the electronics and war industries.

By the time the sixties arrived, I was thoroughly discouraged by the quality of education my children had been subjected to in a variety of communities. If, as I thought, the goal of education was to excite young curiosity and set children on the path toward knowledge, then the teachers and administrators I encountered as a parent and as a reporter had never understood the word. My children put it clearly and directly: "All they care about is drawing their salaries," they patiently explained to me in my childlike innocence.

I thought that perhaps education had fled back to the city. In the hope of finding it, we moved to a low-rent neighborhood not far from the University of California Hospital in San Francisco.

Again, a thirteen-year interval had elapsed between my first return to California, to the metropolitan Bay Area, and my second San Francisco homecoming in 1961. And again, the long time lapse sharpened my focus on the problems and frustrations that I found nagging away at the people all around me.

The problems first visible to Mrs. Rip Van Winkle shortly after World War II had become compounded in this second interval. Now a sense of fear and insecurity prevailed. People began literally to barricade themselves indoors behind iron grilles, guard dogs, arsenals, and alarm systems. They were fearful of going out into the street, and frightened of staying inside alone. They were literally imprisoned by fear.

Noise pollution, pest pollution, the stink of gasoline and diesel fumes, characterized urban life. City dwellers dreamed of escape into the country—then, after "escape," were trapped in endless, frustrating, lonely driving on ever more clogged roads that brought the foul air along with them.

Problems, problems, all God's chillun got problems. The pity was that what I saw on every side, along with futile efforts for personal escape, was an all-pervading sense of personal guilt. There was one phrase even more common than the touching wish "Have a good day," and that was, "I felt so guilty." A deep, pervasive sense of personal guilt, this was the mark of our times, the brand we bore on our foreheads.

Our country, our society, was somehow strangely out of kilter. Something was wrong somewhere and, unable to put their fingers on the root of the problem or to run away from it, our good people were blaming themselves. It is greatly to the credit of our essentially social nature that we shouldered this heavy burden of guilt. But it did not solve the problem, and it certainly hurt the sufferers.

The neighborhood we had moved to was San Francisco's Haight-Ashbury, soon to become famous as the hippie center of the world. Before then, my children had finished growing up and struck out for themselves, and I stayed on to watch the Flower Children and runaways arrive from all parts of the country in their search for community. They were trying to escape, most of them, from prosperous, middle-class homes in which the parents had been trying to escape from their haunting memories of Depression and war with stressful and unfulfilling work, drinking, sedating, and compulsive consumption; television, with its glorification of soap and consumerism, had been the baby-sitter for their generation.

As the seventies began, a friend of more than four decades died and left me a bequest. I decided to reorder what might remain of my own life. I would retire the following year: using half of Anne's bequest for travel and setting aside half for rainy days, I would take one long, foreign journey in my life. I chose a sea voyage to the Southern Hemisphere, and a six-month stay in Latin America. I went with less interest in observing other countries and other wonders, than with the need to gain a fresh perspective on my country and people.

I thought I would come back to a serene, frugal old age—sewing, knitting, cooking for family and friends, spoiling grandchildren. If any spare time was left over, I would take up my journalism and photography again.

The first part of my plan worked better than the second. The effect of inflation on my Social Security, small pension, and nest egg made a return to work necessary. Happily, half-time work would do—with careful budgeting.

The leisure half was too precious to spend doing much sewing or knitting. It was needed for observing, and listening. Listening, I grew aware of the increasingly heavy burden of guilt, confusion, frustration, and stress on every hand, among rich and poor: black, tan, and white; old and young; and as I listened time after time to accounts of ruined relationships, disappointed careers, self-contempt, frustration, stress, and pain, I began to puzzle over the causes.

First I tried reading and listening to scholars, experts, brilliant and respected specialists, but they all seemed to be caught up in some narrow corner or angle of the problem, and then to explore this corner in depth and with authority—for their fellow specialists.

Then I tried reading the newspapers, following running accounts of what was happening in our world, with the emphasis on our country.

Finally, I narrowed down my search still further. I focused on the business news, and then the structure, the skeleton, of our problems came clear. It was like looking through the eye of a needle, which sharpens the view wonderfully.

I'm not that much brighter than average. All I can claim is that a series of circumstances gave me a somewhat more sharply spotlighted overview than many people have. But could I set myself up as an authority, trying to alert others to my own personal insights?

No. I had to wait for a qualified expert to step in. None did. So I gave myself a good shake. Look here, don't count on the experts. It is the plain, simple people who come through when they are needed.

Remember Tom Paine. When the American colonies were baffled, divided, beset by problems with which they could not quite come to grips, there were a lot of brilliant, highly educated men in our country. But it was a plain, simple person with a fresh overview, shaped by a variety of work and workplaces, who was able, in a clear, simple little book, to show the basic issues.

Tom Paine, corset maker, seaman, printer, wrote *Common Sense* in fifty pages. Here, then, is some common sense for the eighties. Remember, it was not the experts on fashion or the specialists on fabric who reported the problem of the emperor's new clothes. Who needs great book learning to know what things most of us find good and want to keep in our country and our time? Our American Dream: the democratic self-government for which we fought and won a revolution; the right to productive and rewarding work; freedom from burdensome taxation; a safe and healthy environment; the opportunity to earn our share of our wonderful, productive industrial output; the full enjoyment of our national characteristic, the capacity for working together for good common goals.

And it doesn't take an expert to name the bad things most of us wish we could *rid* our country of as well as ourselves: continuous and worsening inflation and the unemployment that now seems to fatten it; mounting taxation; swelling bureaucracy; crime, addiction, and mental illness; congestion and loneliness; shortages and glut; the terrible feeling that the government does not represent or care for us, and that to vote is meaningless.

There is one more item on that list, the one most of us try to push out of sight: the fear of nuclear war or atomic disaster—the possibility of an end to all our problems, and of us, too.

This is no how-to-do-it book, with sage instructions for changing our world. It is simply the clearest and most honest view I can present of our problems and their origins. I think it is needed because in our lifetime literally billions of dollars have been spent to confuse each one of us.

It is time to brush aside the lies and confusions so that solutions can be found. In that hope, here is *America Through the Eye of My Needle*. I have written it for my old acquaintances on farms and in fishing villages; for people I've met on jobs and in casual encounters; for concerned friends. Most of all, I have written it for my children and the people like them—busy, hard-working, honest people with no time to spend being intellectual about life but busy living it—people like my daughter the data processor, my son the tanker man, and my daughter-in-law the wife, mother, and grocery checker.

With common sense and renewed understanding and respect for our strong national values, we can make our country beautiful for my grandchildren, for all our grandchildren. And we can do it nonviolently, and in the eighties.

1

wwwwwwwwwwwwwwwwwwwwwwwwwwwwwwwwwwwwwwwwwwwwwwwwww

ROLLED INTO A BALL

There is a kind of late-model rock that makes up many layers of the planet we live on. Geologists have combined two Latin words to name it: *con* and *glomus*, which together mean *gathered into a ball*. Conglomerate rock, then, is made up of older rock fragments annealed with clay, silica, and so forth, usually under pressure.

In the society we are living in now, there is a layering of newer, nongeological kinds of conglomerates. This is how the conglomerate is defined in contemporary dictionaries: "A large corporation formed by the merger of a number of companies in unrelated, widely diversified industries." The definition does not appear in older dictionaries, because the conglomerate is such a recent development in our society. Few of us in fact have given much thought to the impact these new kinds of corporations may be having on our lives.

Start with more than thirty-five years of continuing and worsening inflation. Add the facts that our taxes have inflated along with everything else, that job opportunities have steadily dwindled, that the free-enterprise system has grown ever more anemic nationwide. Mix in a series of recessions partly offset by wars.

Now focus hard on the stresses most of us suffer as direct and indirect results of these conditions, and you will see that we must look for a way of explaining to ourselves these awesome new problems as a first step to solving them.

To begin with basics—today most of the food we eat has been produced, processed, or distributed by conglomerates, whether we purchase it in conglomerate-tied supermarkets, independent mom-and-pop stores, fast-food outlets, health-food stores, or privately owned and operated restaurants.

Most of our clothing is produced by acquired companies, either here or abroad, and the independent store we used to shop at is likely to be part of a conglomerate, as are the bigger, faster clothing chains.

Conglomerates control our public transportation, whether by air, train, or bus, privately owned or leased autos, motorcycles, bikes, mopeds, etc. When we travel, the odds are we will stay in a motel or hotel room owned by a conglomerate.

As for our entertainment—most of the television shows we watch, including the noncommercial, or public, TV programs, appear on conglomerate-owned or -subsidized networks. When we go to a movie, we see the name of a conglomerate flashed on the screen in small letters under the more familiar and conspicuous logo of the producing studio. And most of our reading matter, whether books, magazines, or newspapers, is produced under conglomerate umbrellas. The war matériel that each of us co-owns with our country—if it is true, as claimed,* that one-third of our tax dollars is spent for this purpose—is also conglomerate produced.

The list of conglomerate activities could go on considerably. However, it is long enough here to make it clear that going beyond the simple dictionary definition in our understanding of conglomerates is in our interest.

Here is a description of one conglomerate, quoted from the syndicated newspaper column "Money Tree" by Milt Moskovitz:

> A fairly typical conglomerate is Chesebrough-Pond's, which started in 1955 with a marriage between two old

* Legal arms wholesaler's statement on television's *60 Minutes*, November 5, 1978.

companies: Chesebrough, that had been marketing Vaseline petroleum jelly since 1880, and Pond's (a contemporary of the same vintage, in cosmetics). . . . In 1962 C-P acquired Ragu Spaghetti Sauce, which netted the conglomerate $150 million in 1977, almost the entire C-P net for 1959. . . .[1]

This particular conglomerate, then, came into being a little less than a quarter century ago. The brief description tells of a fast and impressive change in structure through diversification, and an increase in profits that might be called inflated. The phrase "fairly typical" indicates that Chesebrough-Pond's represents one of a considerable number of similar enterprises.

This snippet of information raises certain immediate questions: when, how, and why did corporations begin merging in this way? How many of us work for conglomerates, either knowingly or unknowingly? How much of our income turns into conglomerate profits?

Here is another snippet about conglomerates, reported in Moskovitz's syndicated column, "Money Tree," to partially answer these questions:

The mid 1960's were stock market boom years, and beginning then and continuing until 1970, mergers and acquisitions of large corporations into conglomerates also boomed. . . . In the early 1970's . . . ITT, the biggest of the conglomerates, having become a 160-company conglomerate, was forced by the Courts to divest itself of three smaller companies in order to keep its huge late acquisition: Hartford Insurance Company. . . . By 1977 the timid years were over, and ITT bought 7 more companies, making it the second most active acquirer of the year, way behind Chromalloy American Corporation with 14 acquisitions, giving this conglomerate more than 400 companies, but ahead of Beatrice Foods, the third acquirer with only six new companies. . . .

These rapidly expanding figures, and the recentness of this vast growth, bring us to the sixty-four-dollar question: Do mergers and acquisitions pay?

Pretty well. In 1966 Beatrice Foods sold a piddling $1 billion; its probable sales volume in 1978: $7 billion. But then, ITT has been having annual sales of $13 billion. . . .

In 1946 only ten U.S. companies made over $1 billion in sales; twenty years later, fifty companies; ten years after that, more than three hundred fifty companies. More than one hundred sixty of these had sales of $2 billion or more that year (1976).

By now it is clear that conglomerates have been thriving during the more than a quarter century in which inflation has been causing so many of us so many problems. If we remember that this has been the first time in history that inflation has continued, uninterrupted, over an extended period, and that during this same era an entirely new economic and social arrangement has grown up, it seems likely that a cause-and-effect relationship exists between inflation and conglomerates.

The test of the hypothesis appears to lie in this question: could company after company have made profits in the billions of dollars if the currency had remained stable or fluctuated in both directions? Or, on the other hand, was inflation necessary to this remarkable growth?

The answer must surely be that inflation is necessary for the raking in of those inflated profits. It is difficult to believe that, without inflation to make such profits possible, Chromalloy American Corporation, an unfamiliar name to this writer and probably to most readers, could have started out some time within the past quarter century or not much earlier, possibly with just one company, and in that short time acquired 399 more.

Conglomerates profit from inflation. Accept this simple statement as a working hypothesis, and then read the business portion of your daily paper for a week or so. To do so sounds dreary, but it isn't, really. For one thing, this section is usually combined with all or part of the sports section; for another, it is terse. The news is briefly reported for busy readers. There are none of the usual human-interest puffery or public-relations items about the families and pets of the tenants of the White House, the government mansion, or mayoral office; or the statements of good intentions by hopeful political candidates. Instead, the financial section reports general news of fluctuations in the stock market, the value of the dollar, inflation, unemployment rates, and fuel shortages or gluts. It reports changes in the number of billions of dollars owned by us, the American taxpayers. Such is the general business news: news of fluctuations.

The specific news items deal almost entirely with two matters. The first is the astronomical profits of a variety of the five hundred or so companies in the country whose finances are worthy of report, and who are required by law to report such matters. (Some giants are family businesses, like Bechtel Corporation, and so are spared public scrutiny.)

The other type of specific news item deals with something the financial reporters have given a name to: merger mania. It appears from these news items that an almost frenzied activity is in progress among the conglomerates and some of the great corporations that try to pretend they are not really conglomerates (the airlines, for example). This activity is the business of merging with each other, of acquiring or being acquired, of diversifying. Rumors and reports about the methods used in these activities are news, especially when the giant company or conglomerate targeted for acquisition violently objects, or the government questions the legality of the proposed merger.

In 1979, one example of such newsworthy merger plans involved McGraw-Hill, the publishing conglomerate, which didn't want to be acquired by American Express. F. W. Woolworth, in the same year, had no wish to become part of Branscan Ltd. of Canada. These companies were among the few who managed not to be swallowed whole.

As noted earlier, the rise and explosive development of the conglomerates paralleled the first period we have ever experienced of extended, uninterrupted inflation. Suppose we found that during this same period the cancerous growth of those other serious national woes took place. We might conclude that a connection existed between conglomeratism and the problems that weave through the fabric of all our lives, that plague us in a variety of ways.

Look at them one by one. Hard on the heels of the problem of inflation is the problem of unemployment.

UNEMPLOYMENT

It is clear that something besides inflation is needed to produce the great conglomerate profits. Otherwise, all businesses would have made inflated profits, and they have not. This other requirement is given several names in financial jargon: "cost effectiveness," "rationalization," * and "the bottom line."

The bottom line is the net profit, and this depends on cost effectiveness, which may require rationalization. Cost effectiveness is the profitable production per work unit. Thus, to be cost effective a company must rationalize its operations—that is, it must get rid of anything that interferes with the cost effectiveness of each work unit. In translation, this means firing people and replacing them with machines.

The acquiring company has rationalized its operations to produce maximum cost effectiveness, and thus a favorable bottom line, which has given it the cash or credit necessary to acquire another company or to effect a profitable merger.

The company being acquired may not have been so businesslike. It must have profit potential, or the acquiring company wouldn't be interested in it (unless it needs another tax shelter, which sometimes happens). Its uninflated, or sometimes even red bottom line, which makes it open to the offer or raid of the

---

* *Rationalization* is the jargon for taking action to produce more profit per work unit. A work unit is the amount of manufacturing productivity or output produced by one worker in one hour. Ironically, after years of conglomerate rationalizing, U.S. productivity is rated sixth of the seven most industrialized nations by the U.S. Department of Labor (Associated Press, *San Francisco Chronicle,* July 11, 1979, p. 25).

acquiring company, might indicate that its operations are not cost effective and need rationalizing.

These conditions may have resulted from a lack of sufficient capital or credit to invest in machines to replace unprofitable work units, or to move operations to a region or country with cheaper work units. Or they might indicate that the company's management hung on too long to the old-fashioned notion that its staff were human beings, or that it had some obligation to the community that had grown to depend upon it. If they were unable to view their employees as cost-effective units, management may have been unable to fire any of them to rescue their bottom line.

There may be statistics somewhere of how many employees, white-collar and blue, eventually lost out when the 399 companies they were part of were acquired, one by one, by Chromalloy American Company, for instance. We don't need statistics to tell us that the number of company chief executive officers (CEOs, a popular term in financial jargon) shrank from 399 to somewhere around zero.

We know that, although large segments of office and agricultural workers have become unionized, union membership throughout the country has been shrinking by a third through attrition of the workforce since the end of World War II, when the corporations began merging into conglomerates. According to the *Handbook of Labor Statistics* published by the United States Department of Labor, there was a rise in the proportion of unionized workers from 1935, when it was 6.7 percent, to 1957, when it was 24.9 percent, after which the percentage decreased, standing at 21.8 percent in 1971, 1972, and 1973.[2] (Reports are given only through 1973.)

We also know that in addition to the hundreds of thousands now accepted as necessarily unemployed, or tagged "hard-core unemployables," two large segments of the nation's workforce seem to grow as the whole force shrinks: the criminal-justice system and the whole governmental bureaucracy of which the criminal-justice system is a grim and costly portion.

MENTAL AND SOCIAL SICKNESS

These two woes of our time have also been developing during much the same period, and at the same rate, as the conglomerates. Is there a cause-and-effect relationship here, also? The question must be raised, because if such a relationship does not exist, the conglomerates should be exonerated from the suspicion that one does.

If one of the 500 giant corporations in our country acquires 399 formerly more or less private, diversified enterprises, common sense tells us that the pressures and stresses of all these mergers and absorptions in so short a time must affect many private enterprises, many family farms, mom-and-pop stores, and small factories in the country. By the simplest of mathematics, let us multiply this process by 500 and let us say that during the same period roughly 200,000 private enterprises were swallowed by conglomerates. It is easy to imagine the widespread disorientation felt during this period of stress.

In the past two decades a lie has been created. A massive public-relations program has been carried on to convince the American public that the conglomerates are representatives of the very free-enterprise system they are actually squeezing out of existence. The quality of Ragu spaghetti sauce, for example, is compared in commercials to that of "the free-enterprise system that produces it." The slogan, thought up by an advertising copywriter, to be aired over conglomerate TV networks, is intended to boost the sales of Chesebrough-Pond's. The Ragu slogan bears thinking about, not just because the sentiment it expresses is a lie, but because the lie is tailored to our national love for free enterprise, for the American Dream of some day each of us being our own boss or at least having a say about how we make our living. This dream is at the heart of our national character.

Reflect, then, on the names of the conglomerates in this context. Some are the homey names, such as Beatrice Foods, that invoke an image of something simple and folksy. Others, such as those of most banks, insurance companies, and other financial institutions, use national or local place names to invoke the image of patriotism or of regional ties: Chromalloy American, for instance.*

No need to belabor the point that a great deal of money is being spent to give us switched signals, to fill us with national ardor for our native ideal of democratic equality in free enterprise at the very time when most of the democracy is being squeezed out of our national economy. Remember Pavlov's famous experiments in psychology—he drove dogs mad by accustoming them to a set of rewards for certain actions, and then switched the rewards to punishments for the same activities.

Other factors in our lives during this present era, the era of the conglomerates, might bear upon the unusual increase of mental and social sickness among our people. We can't blame conglomerates for having set us as a nation on a restless course. There were no dedicated stay-at-homes among our settlers, that goes without saying. Having settled, the more adventurous, restless, or needy pioneers kept on the move in other ways. Yet stability and community were usually ideals. Immigrants sought out and found locales similar to their homelands, their old countries, and created communities in them. Town halls flourished throughout the country; families sank roots that extended into their communities. Regional dialects, sometimes incomprehensible to people from other regions, were developed and preserved, and the pockets of distinctive cultures enriched the nation.

The years of the Great Depression, the 1930s, brought a change in the quantity of flux. The change was so great that it in turn effected a change in the quality of social relationships. The people of the Dust Bowl, and the unemployed of cities and towns, took to the roads to search out means of survival, as did

---

* True, there are exceptions. An earth-girdling copper company, Anaconda, did name itself for the boa constrictor. And our biggest U.S. conglomerate, International Telephone and Telegraph (ITT) proudly heralded its international ties. But those names were chosen in an earlier day. Was it, possibly, a more honest day? Conglomerates change, too, and so does their choice of names. The present trend is for the most impersonal of initials, e.g., NLT, MGI Investment, SCM.

their children, orphaned and hungry, who traveled in packs. Many survived, and settled wherever the chances of survival were greatest.

When the war industries started up and ended the Depression, their industrialists set up shop where they found the greatest pools of labor, cheap labor. Industrialists still do this— always on the move, within and outside our country, they take their dollars and their machinery and their know-how away from areas of prosperity—and thus away from those who demand prosperity-producing salaries and wages—to the poor places of the nation and world. Each such move has left people, families, and whole communities more or less stranded, their accustomed source of earnings lifted out of their lives.

Each move by an industry has also carried with it the relocation of key personnel and their families, and this trend was soon found to be cost-effective for the movers. First, it served as a test of loyalty to the company. "Leave thy father and thy mother and thy brother," says an ancient Persian love song. What stronger proof of loyalty to the company could employees show than the willingness to leave all but wife and children, and sometimes them too, at the company's bidding. To pass this test, employees have had to leave behind all ties to church and friends and to extended families, as well as shared memories and interests. They have had to move to new communities where the strongest tie is to the company itself and the greatest reward is money and the material things that money can buy. Monetary compensation to make up for the social pleasures, the deep sense of belonging, and so of identity, those intangible qualities that are lost in the move—at least until new roots are sunk. These corporate-inspired moves are particularly difficult for wives, who usually do not even have the continuity of work to substitute for their lost community. Infrequently, it is a woman who moves, with the man either tagging along or staying behind. What have these chess-pawn moves, which have taken place by the thousands and tens of thousands, done to the children of relocated families?

What they have done to the mental and social health of the

country as a whole can be seen by a glance at the statistics. During the era when many free or relatively free enterprises have been growing, merging, and diversifying into conglomerates, the rate of mental and social illness has increased markedly. The conditions involved include depression, weight problems, drinking problems, drug addiction, compulsive gambling, learning and working disabilities, hyperactivity, violent behavior, child abuse, rape, mayhem, murder, and suicide. Also during this time, family patterns have changed; the extended family has given way to the nuclear-family unit, composed of parents or parent and children or child. Simultaneously, the marriage rate has fallen, the divorce rate risen, and marriage as an institution has become almost too stressed to be workable.

Clearly, crime is also a part of the mental and social sickness whose increase has paralleled the growth of the conglomerates, those economic structures that rose from the ashes of the American Dream.

POLLUTION OF OUR AIR, WATER, AND LAND

The connection between the destruction of our physical environment with our new economic order hardly needs pointing out. At any rate, the connection in time is obvious. Viewing pollution in this context raises some thoughts about cost effectiveness and rationalization. For instance, many environmental problems arise from the assumption that the creators of problems are entitled to the profits produced but are not responsible for the cost of solving the problems they created along the way. As they see it, solving those problems is the responsibility of the rest of us—the taxpayers.

THE THREAT OF WAR

The mushroom-shaped cloud was young when Chesebrough and Pond's were married, but inflation, prosperity, and super-profits have been threatened three times since that first atomic explosion. In that period, three separate recessions began to plague the economy. Each time, the threat of recession was averted: first by the cold war, then by the Korean War, then by the Vietnam War. Instead of recession, inflation continued, and so did inflated profits, and greater diversification, and more and bigger mergers.

Now in the financial pages, we find frequent hints of another impending recession. And the conglomerates are trying a variation on the theme of war to solve the problem of threatened recession: our country has become the world's merchant in arms to all the troubled spots of the earth. Including our own.

☆

If the conglomerates are the fountainhead of so many of our present problems, then it is up to us to find out whether we can do anything about them. The first step is to discover how on earth, in a democracy, a land founded by revolution on the principle of equal opportunity, these giants were allowed to come into being, and whether they are legal and constitutional entities.

The chairman of the Federal Trade Commission raised these very questions on May 7, 1979, at an antitrust seminar sponsored by Time Inc., and reported by the Associated Press. Michael Pertschuk, chairman of the Federal Trade Commission, was quoted as saying:[3]

> The trend toward mergers is posing dangers to the American political system . . . the formation of conglomerate firms continues to increase . . . two dozen $100-million mergers were announced in the first quarter of 1979, almost twice as many as during the same period last year.
>
> The danger posed by the surge toward increasingly large firms is encroachment upon the viability of bedrock institutions: a free market, a responsive political system, a pluralistic society. . . .

As an example of the ability of a huge firm to influence political decisions, Pertschuk cited the campaign by General Motors to postpone the implementation of safety and emission standards. He said the giant automaker "solicited support through letters to its 13,000 dealers, 19,000 suppliers and 1.3 million stockholders." He also said that the Business Roundtable, a group of the top business executives in the nation, has emerged as "the pre-eminent lobbying institution in Washington."

Pertschuk said this development

> signifies the emergence of political activism as a first priority of the corporate manager. And the visibility and direct personal involvement of chief executive officers removes any shadow of a doubt that aggressive political activity has become not only respectable, but the hallmark of a corporate leader . . . enhancing the absolute political power of the merged firms.

A thoughtful reading of the FTC chairman's remarks is both heartening and frightening. For me, the heartening component was that Pertschuk's language and his turns of phrase marked him as a product of the class and educational background from which the powerful business lobby allows its regulatory bodies to be selected. This man was not addressing some dissident, left-wing group, but a seminar sponsored by one of the most conservative and powerful publishing combines in the country, Time Inc. Yet he spoke out clearly and courageously on behalf of true democracy, removal of the power over our government which has been stolen by the conglomerates from the people who had won it with the Declaration of Independence and the Constitution.

The frightening implication of Pertschuk's remarks was that the conglomerates would make every possible move to destroy any honest, democratic threat to their control of the government.

☆

On September 19, 1979, an open attack on the FTC was made by the Kellogg Company at a Subcommittee on Consumer Affairs hearing in the Senate. According to a United Press article, the Kellogg Company was locked in two disputes with the commission at the time of the hearing "over proposed regulation of television commercials directed at children, especially for sugary cereals, and an antitrust case seeking to break up major cereal companies." Attorneys for the American Medical Association and Kellogg Company were demanding adjustments of the laws under which the FTC operated. They wanted Congress to have veto power over the agency—in other words, to take away its power to act. Subcommittee Chairman Senator Wendell Ford was sympathetic to these demands. He was quoted as saying he knew of "no other agency that has aroused the ire of my constituents like the FTC." The senator was demonstrating, as other representatives have, that his real constituents are not the consumers but the conglomerates.

2

~~~~~~

CARS AND THEIR COUSINS

"How did the conglomerates ever make their entry into our egalitarian and democratic society and our free-enterprise social structure in the first place?"

"They rode the rails."

An unlikely answer to the question? Unlikely, but true.

Our Constitution was drafted in 1787, after the American Revolution but before the Industrial Revolution had reached the Western Hemisphere. Its terms were designed to safeguard us from ever developing an aristocracy based on feudal land holdings.

Nobody could foresee that in the following century industrialism and the invention of the railroad would lead to the creation of an aristocracy of power based on wealth: greater wealth and greater power than that of the hated landed aristocracy of Europe.

When the locomotive was first invented, it took a lot of imagination and daring on the part of bankers and financiers to risk their money—and their depositors' money—on railroad building in this vast, still poor, and undeveloped land. These men of money hedged their risks by insisting on the greatest land grab in history: the government was convinced to cede every tenth square mile along the rights of way to the railroad companies. With this arrangement, the unwritten rule of the moneymen was established: To us go the profits; to *them* (meaning the taxpayers, or us), the costs.

Soon this efficient formula paid off for the investors. When the trains began to roll, their routes led through farm and grazing lands, towns and cities, into forests and mining territory. Along these routes were privately owned, comparatively small enterprises: family farms, stores, and shops; factories owned and operated by partners. But not long after the railroads started hauling their products into market, the ownership of these enterprises began to change. The railroads, with their money and their power over press and politicians, had absolute power over the producers. They preferred to have a smaller number of large producers, so large numbers of small producers were squeezed out. A new class began to arise—the middlemen.

The speed and efficiency of the railroad's movement, the vastness of its range, had created a new set of values. Money began to flow out of small, local banks into the great financial centers of Wall Street. Grain and livestock were funneled into the markets of Chicago and carried along localized and region-centered business. Profit and loss turned into a monstrous game—a gamble that at times brought prosperity, and at times bankruptcy, to pawns and players.

Most publishers and politicians soon learned that it was to their interest to grab hold of the coattails of the rising class. Speculation became a way of life, with monopoly its goal, and the periods between boom and bust on a local level and often nationwide rarely lasted a dozen years. Each boom and each bust sucked more wealth up to the top, blew down more poverty through middle and base.

The new aristocrats were called magnates: an appropriate sound-alike for magnets—they and money attracted each other. The voters, whose grandparents had hated the pomp of foreign aristocrats, were encouraged to admire the flamboyant home-grown kind as the American Dream come true. They saw these men as famous, successful, and respected throughout the world; boasting beautiful, bejeweled women, palatial houses with battalions of servants, and private railroad cars, yachts, and blooded horses. These were models parents could hold up to their children, paragons of industry and ambition. The new aristocracy was glorified in the press and on stage, in all the arts, and from the pulpits too, for from it flowed a golden stream of patronage, philanthropy, and piety.

As the nineteenth century grew old, however, all was not admiration for the magnates. The new mills and factories needed more and cheaper hands, and brought them in from assorted poverty areas in Europe and Asia. Most work-seeking immigrants came with a vision of the democracy and equality they would find when they reached the shores of America. When they found slums, with wild fluctuations of work and unemployment, living wages and pittances, and financial panics following booms, they began to see the new aristocrats not as symbols of the American Dream, but as its enemies.

In England and on the Continent, an intellectual ferment had been brewing since the beginning of the Machine Age. First came the utopian socialists, thoughtful middle- and upper-class idealists who might be environmentalists today. They hated the pollution created by railroads and factories, and sought to found pockets of utopian work-sharing in the midst of seething change. Then came the anarchists, who proclaimed that humankind would live in peace and dignity if all government was done away with. Then the economic socialists emerged, whose leading prophets were Karl Marx and Friedrich Engels. These thinkers predicted that capitalism would destroy itself and so make way for ownership of the means of production by all the people who produced.

These ideas bubbled up across our country, too, whenever times were bad. Desperate farmers and mine, mill, and lumber workers rallied around their spokespeople. But these ideas were never absorbed into the American temperament, never replaced the ideals of free enterprise, of proud self-sufficiency, of equality of opportunity. Anyway, there were still frontiers, at home and abroad, to keep hope alive and to drain away the restless.

The yeast remained. The ferment spread through the country, heating up during hard times, cooling down during times of prosperity. But even in prosperous times the conviction began to go deeper and grow firmer that monopoly was a threat to democracy, that too much power in too few hands meant danger to independent ownership, whether of farm or business. Equally threatened were the wage-earners who labored within these enterprises.

The feeling against the monopolies grew so strong that by 1890 it resulted in the passage of the Sherman Antitrust Act. Congress passed the act even though President Benjamin Harrison was on the side of the big industrialists. The Antitrust Act was weak. Popular sentiment had demanded action; business influence watered it down. Against the feeble efforts of the lukewarm courts, the trusts and monopolies kept on growing.

The nineteenth century ended in financial panics and militancy within the growing labor movement. Writers and artists began to reflect what they saw in popular terms. As the twentieth century began, a son of the wealthy class rode shouting into political power as the Great Trust Buster.

Theodore Roosevelt's background and affiliations were with the wealthy. Maybe it was from them he learned the value of image building. Through vigorous efforts, he made himself known to the voters as hard-riding, hard-working, Eastern-trust-hating Teddy. When he became president, he kept right on railing against the trusts. And the trusts kept on growing. Meanwhile Teddy became an empire builder, grabbing Panama from Colombia and Cuba from Spain.

Still, with the growth of the trusts, opposition grew. The muckraking journalist Ida M. Tarbell published *The History of the Standard Oil Company* in 1904. Shortly afterward the Clayton Antitrust Act was passed and the Federal Trade Commission established. Seven years later the Supreme Court "broke up" Standard Oil, a Rockefeller monopoly.

With it all, the power of the trusts and monopolies kept right on growing. World War I helped. The war followed our military excursions into the Central American banana republics, the Philippines, and Mexico.

It helped, too, that the tycoons had learned some important lessons. Less flamboyant now, except for a few of their sons, they kept a low profile. Most magnates used their influence to stay out of the limelight, except as doers of good works.

A whole new profession grew up and prospered. Its forerunners had started modestly, as barkers and publicists for circuses and freak shows; now educated and talented writers, artists, and idea people were attracted into the profession of public relations and advertising.

The law prospered, too. Finding ways for wealthy clients to comply with the letter of the antitrust acts while ignoring their spirit created cartels of wealthy and powerful lawyers.

But a new power was rising in the land that was to triumph against the monopolies of the railroads where the Clayton Act and all the efforts of courts and regulatory agencies had met a stone wall. The creators of this new force began by learning everything the railroads had to teach—and then squeezing the teachers in a vise.

The automobile had arrived.

☆

In 1973, the Arab oil embargo and resulting empty gas tanks brought home to us the fact that one income in every six in our country depends either directly or indirectly on the existence of the car.

Sure, the car was always central in the thoughts of most of us—we thought a great deal about very specific matters relating to the pros and cons of specific cars, past, present, and future. But 1973 set us all thinking more broadly—and less cheerfully. It raised frightening questions: without the car, what would we do? We had to have the car. Without it, there would be physical, financial, and social disaster, both individually and nationally. But we never asked whether there was any solution except to keep driving until the earth's supply of fossil fuel was exhausted or the planet destroyed—or how we got into such a fix in the first place.

We got into it in three stages. The first stage was the invention and early creation of the horseless carriage. Its creators were mechanics and artisans, inventors, and craftsmen, working in carriage houses and smithies, all lovingly and expensively crafting the early cars. The cars themselves served as status symbols for the rich, playthings for their children.

On the appearance of the Iron Horse, the railroad locomotive, prophets had foretold that the flesh-and-blood horse would soon be an extinct species. It is doubtful that anyone, during Phase I of the car story, could have predicted that soon the horseless carriage would make the iron horse an endangered species.

Phase 2 began when, as every schoolkid knows, Henry Ford ventured to make automobiles that "the poor man could afford." We all know that Ford created this miracle with assembly-line mass production. We forget that what Ford meant by the "poor man" was not what the term means today, in the third phase of the car story.

Ford's poor men belonged to the class below the rich industrial aristocracy, but formed a class with the means or the need to keep buggies or saddle horses: doctors, lawyers, preachers, farmers, politicians, storekeepers, small businessmen. Also included were the more successful and solvent segment of that class called "mechanics": printers, railroad engineers, and shop foremen. These were people able to save enough money beyond the cost of necessities to pay cash for a car. The car finance system had yet to be invented. Ford increased his market of poor-man car owners by paying his assembly-line workers double the going wage and shortening their work day to eight hours. Thus he created a blue-collar elite, the first factory workers in the country's history able to save enough beyond the necessities of life to buy a nonessential item (if they managed to do the saving while they were still young and strong enough to stand the pace of the assembly line, and so continue to be employable) and with enough leisure for enjoyment. Ford may have foreseen that other factory owners would be forced to follow his example, and so add to his market.

Most of the population, even after the creation of this first labor elite, was below the car-buying level. The rural and urban poor embraced all the ethnic minorities—and of course women who had to work to support themselves and often their families. Few among the minorities were exceptions to the rule of poverty. Those poor men, far from being the "poor man" of whom Ford talked, rarely owned even a horse, mule, or bicycle.

The railroads had three valuable lessons to teach the new automotive industry during this second phase of its development, which lasted from Ford's first assembly line to the end of World War II. The first was, Beware of becoming a monopoly; avoid even the appearance of being a trust or a cartel. Second, Load as much of the costs of the new mode of travel onto the public as possible, and so keep the profits clear. And, third, Never neglect the image makers or fail to encourage them to influence the press and politicians whenever possible.

The railroads had helped to finance the building of their systems with a great land grab, but they still had to maintain tracks, bridges, tunnels, snow fences, stations, and rolling stock. They received only comparatively modest government subsidies for carrying the mails. In contrast, once autos were made and sold and the terms of a simple warranty met, the responsibility of the manufacturers ended.

Road building and maintenance were at first the only costs to the public, but even those expenses were considerable, since roads for cars cost more than roads for horse-drawn vehicles. Still, in the second phase, the costs of cars to the public were not exorbitant. Of course, the maintenance costs for car owners were considerably higher than the costs of train or streetcar tickets, by which public transportation was supported (with a profit left over for the carriers). But during this second phase of the car story, our autos still reflected the essence of our national character: they allowed us to express our love for free choice, equality, mobility, and fun. And, they confirmed our basic belief that work and economizing should be rewarded materially.

For Ford, and for his imitators and competitors, a problem soon arose: the car became too profitable. When the most successful tycoons of the earlier era began to reap superprofits, they used the money to smash or buy out their next largest competitors, and thus gain control of the market.

When the automakers became successful, they did squeeze out, buy out, or merge with company after company, but they stopped far short of monopoly. The lessons of the Sherman and Clayton acts and the public revolt against Standard Oil had been taken to heart; thus, even today we have four automobile manufacturers in the United States. This is known as free competition. Any appearance of collusion on price fixing, for example, is purely coincidental.

All the same, the profits of the auto industry had to be put to work to make bigger profits, monopoly or no monopoly. There was a limit to how much could be channeled into foundations and other philanthropic and public-relations uses. The solution was diversification: the production of tractors and other farm equipment and trucks. When Chevrolet became General Motors, household appliances and an increasing variety of machinery and supplies were added.

The early assembly line had literally been an *assembly* line. Many of the parts assembled into the final products were manufactured by privately owned producers and patent holders. For my generation (and I'm now seventy) large and glamorous billboards advertising "Bodies by Fisher" were as familiar as ads today for Fords or Chevrolets. Fisher designed and produced bodies for several manufacturers. Today, the name means nothing.

When World War I broke out, Henry Ford, either from altruism or because he thought peace, not war, sold cars, helped to finance, back, and sail a "Peace Ship" to Europe to try to persuade the enemies to arbitrate. The effort was defeated with press ridicule, and the early "peacenik" opened his River Rouge plant and tooled up for war.

These were the developments of the automakers up to the end of World War II. At that time, we were still in Phase 2 of the age of the auto. A vast market had been created, by both the soft and hard sell, for the privately owned car, abroad and especially at home. The thrust of the sell was to make people *want* to own cars.

The sell, for which many millions of dollars had been paid out over the years, started in the kindergarten and continued to the motorized hearse at the end. We were sold on the idea of owning a car via schoolbooks, movies, radio, magazines, newspapers, show rooms, billboards, ads, stories, pictures, and songs. The car symbolized sexual adequacy, both male and female: for men it represented the glittering metallic plumage of the courting male bird; for women it was a seductive invitation to beauty—an open door revealed a soft, luxurious interior. For both men and women, the created longing for a car was an aching, orgasmic wish that often led to car theft, joy rides, and casual, ungratifying seductions.

And cars led to death. The annual toll, especially among the young, soon marked the car as a more lethal weapon than the handgun. All the same, during Phase 2, the car did not violate the essential American character. It made jobs for many small-business people: car salesmen, mechanics, service-station owners and operators, and owners of garages and roadside businesses. And, still, to buy or not to buy was optional.

The end of World War II ushered in Phase 3, the phase in which we are living today. Car manufacture had been limited by military necessity during the war. But by the time the war had ended, the companies had reaped vast war profits. And the immediate demand for private vehicles was great: every car owner needed a new car, and in that prosperous time could afford the replacement.

The wise manufacturers knew it was time to look to the future. One step was to export wartime profits to countries with lower wages or a favorable dollar exchange, or both: our recent allies, and our recently hated enemies. They built plants abroad for parts manufacture, assembly, and sale, which began to compete with the home production. Here and at home, the capital available for tooling up for Phase 3 remained abundant.

Developing the market for Phase 3, unlike the efforts needed for the previous phase, required more than just direct advertising and publicity based on simple appeals to desire, though of course those measures were not neglected. Phase 3 involved selling not the *wish* for a car, but the *need* for a car, not just to those who could afford the pleasure, but to those who could not afford to buy a car. The industry had to make these people too dependent on car ownership as a life-support system to afford to get along without one.

Creation of the need had to be done more subtly and ingeniously than a drug pusher's hooking of a prospective customer.

Happily for the manufacturers, the vast industry had attracted several powerful satellites: the tire manufacturers, the metals industries, the insurance business, the finance structure of banks and companies, the distributors, and the union members in all these vast and recently unionized enterprises. Most valuable of all was the already powerful fuel industry.

Clearly, automakers and their satellites had tremendous clout with the media as well as political clout at all levels. The industry used its clout to make the privately owned car the only way to go. Until World War II, public transportation had been available and was adequate for most who did not live in remote spots. Not anymore!

Former San Francisco Mayor Joseph L. Alioto, a shrewd and knowledgeable corporation lawyer, told one story in a newspaper interview of how the clout was used. The San Francisco Oakland Bay Bridge had been built in the late twenties and early thirties by popular vote and with public money. It had a deck for passenger cars, and a deck below for trucks and for the rapid transit system of the day: the Key Route railed trolley trains.

During the war, wartime priorities had resulted in the neglect of the public system. Simultaneously, the local population had increased manyfold because the war industries had attracted workers from the nation's poverty pockets. Naturally, at war's end the public system needed a great deal more rolling stock to accommodate this increased need, and the neglected tracks and equipment needed overhauling.

At that point, said Alioto, the General Motors lobby persuaded the authorities to *tear out the tracks*, close down the system, and open the second level to cars. It was GM's argument that buses (GM by choice) would serve the public more cheaply than the trains. Once the tracks were out and the Key Route trains scrapped, the inadequate bus schedules were cut back time and again, in accordance with the self-fulfilling prophecy that people would prefer driving their own cars to riding the buses.

This iceberg tip of Phase 3 of the automobile era bobbed into view almost by chance. That the same pattern was being followed everywhere in the country once the auto industry began exercising its lobbying clout does not have to be dug out proof by proof. The proof is in today's almost total absence nationwide of any fully adequate public transportation (except air transport, which augments rather than replaces auto use). Over the years, passenger train service everywhere has been cut back. What was allowed to remain has deteriorated and become increasingly expensive. Today, our railroads are heavily subsidized by the taxpayers, and at the very time they are insisting that they cannot afford to provide commuter and passenger service, they are negotiating and buying unrelated businesses. During this same period, Greyhound, the almost-monopoly bus service, had cut back schedules and raised the fares for increasingly filthy buses and facilities.

My city, San Francisco, is said to have one of the best public-transportation systems in the country, the Muni. If this is true, heaven help the worst. The five-minute intervals in the trolley schedules of my school days, a half century ago, are now up to twelve minutes during the jam-packed commuter periods, and twenty minutes afterward. Later in the evening, when to stand on a street corner is to stand in fear, Muni buses run every forty minutes at each transfer point.

By 1970, the one-car family remained practical only for one-person families, and the lack of realistic public transportation made it necessary for each family member old enough to drive to have some sort of wheels.

By 1978, the average cost of car maintenance had risen to $1,500 per year. (Health care cost us $160 billion in 1978; $376 billion was spent caring for our cars and trucks.)[1] At last report, a fifth of all our incomes were being channeled into car purchase.

In campaign season (Is it ever closed season these days?), the fact that many welfare recipients own some sort of car is usually made much of and cited as evidence of welfare pampering. Car possession is allowed by welfare agencies only when it is shown to be essential for survival. It is doubtful that the car manufacturers sincerely oppose this use of tax funds.

Each decade the proliferation rate of cars increased. In the 1950s it rose by 2.2 million a year, in the 1960s by 3.7 million, and in the 1970s by 4.4 million a year.[2] And so the supersaturation point approached. By the early sixties even the automakers began to realize that there was a limit to how much bumper-to-bumper driving the human spirit could endure. At that point, Band-Aid relief began to appear in the form of a revival of carefully meted out, minimally effective public transportation systems. In the San Francisco Bay Area, for example, in 1963, the publicly financed, three-county Bay Area Rapid Transit (BART) was voted in. After years of work and many increases in the originally accepted and astronomical cost, a poorly engineered system is now in partial operation. Maybe BART should be described not as a Band-Aid, but as a tourniquet. When on January 17, 1979, a fire in the transbay tube (between San Francisco and Oakland) closed down the system, cars flooded the Bay Bridge; that nightmare time about which many have fantasized—when all traffic would snarl beyond ever unsnarling—appeared to be at hand.

In the San Francisco Bay Area there have been a few more Band-Aids: the Golden Gate Bridge Authority has put on buses and bought some ferries, and Greyhound has cleaned up its buses, facilities, and image.

Public pressure, though still opposed by auto-industry lobbies, has changed the strange requirement that all gasoline taxes be spent on highways. Some of these monies are now channeled into public transportation.

Until recently conglomerates have followed the policy of keeping a low profile, but lately (apparently for purposes of financial prestige) some have come out in the open. Note, for example, the text of a full-page ad run by Greyhound in 1978 in the two San Francisco daily papers:

> Greyhound is a lot of things that might surprise you. Like big. Based on revenues, *Fortune* lists Greyhound as the 49th largest U.S. industrial with 1976 sales of over $3.7 billion.
>
> And diversified. Greyhound's activities run from transportation to food to soap to computer leasing to restaurants to display contracting to jet fueling systems at major airports and more. . . .
>
> Greyhound is the number one transportation company on earth . . . or in the sky. In 1976, we carried 25 million more people than America's number two carrier, United Airlines . . . we own more jets than some airlines. . . .
>
> In short, Greyhound isn't just "the bus company" any more, it's "the omnibus company."

So, next time you phone Greyhound for schedule information, after you have dialed a few times and heard busy signals, and a machine answers, saying, "Thank you for calling the Greyhound Information Center. All our operators are busy at this time . . ." don't reflect angrily that your common carrier is failing in its public responsibility by not hiring enough operators to provide needed public service. Be proud that your om-

nibus system has made *Fortune*'s top 50 with all that soap and
jet transport. What if holding the line does cause you to miss
your bus? With luck, there might be another on the same day.

The cost of such an ad is not public information, but if it only
ran in those U.S. cities as large or larger than San Francisco,
the money spent on the newspaper space could pay the annual
salary of a number of switchboard operators.

To return to the car manufacturers: they have been stalling
for years on seriously attempting to provide smog-free, fossil-
fuel-saving, affordable cars. They cope with safety hazards only
when public outcry and substantial court damage settlements
outweigh their profit.

Now we are well into Phase 3 of the car story. Our annual
death toll from highway accidents even with a lowered speed
limit, stood at almost forty-seven thousand in 1977.[3] Not included in that statistic are deaths from cancer, emphysema,
and heart trouble, diseases now known to be related to smog
and stress. No one questions that the existence of the latter is
related on many levels to traffic and other transportation-
related problems.

Not included either are the numbers of crippling physical in-
juries (we call them mayhem when the offender is human),
emotional tragedies, and financial disasters caused by autos and
other wheeled vehicles. Some insight into the magnitude of
these numbers might be glimpsed each time we drive past a
wrecking yard, its mountain of crumpled steel glinting dully in
sunlight or headlamp. Or when our insurance bill arrives with
its usual increase.

For the most part, we try not to think of these unpleasant
side effects of our essential and treasured cars. So it is not hard
to divorce them in our minds from those other unpleasant
aspects of our lives: the horrifying crime rate, the decay of our
cities, and the increase of bureaucracy and taxes.

And we are even more likely to close our eyes to the link between the automobile and the isolation and inhumanity that
fills so much of our lives: the lonely drives, the city streets,

sidewalks, and promenades that used to pulse night and day but are now empty of socializers, churchgoers, theatergoers, and promenaders. These lively throngs still exist in many other countries, but not in ours.

Every morning, as I walk through my middle-to-low-income neighborhood, I pass hundreds of thousands of dollars worth of cars parked along the curbs and on the sidewalks. They are parked so close to one another and to the buildings that often I must walk out into the middle of the street to go around them. Most of these cars are left out unprotected. They are vulnerable to fog or rain, vandalism, stripping, and outright theft, either by youthful joyriders or hard-working professionals in the big business of auto theft.*

Most cars are not left out by the owner's choice. For most owners, their car is still their most valuable investment, although intentional car thievery is becoming a common form of insurance fraud. Quite simply, it is not in the interests of the car industry to plan for garaging for cars or even full protection from theft. Quite the opposite: susceptibility to damage and theft is good for sales and a powerful adjunct to the built-in obsolescence of the product.

Talk to a friend, neighbor, or bus rider about cars and the conversation will always end this way: "But there's no way out. We Americans are so hooked on our cars that nothing will change us until the supply of fuel runs out." If this is so, do not think too harshly of yourself or your fellow citizens, but reflect on the billions of dollars spent both on the hard sell and soft sell and on the corruption of politicians and press, direct or subtle, to get us hooked.

We are no more stupid than the people who created our fix. Just less ruthless.

Phase 3 of the automobile era will certainly end some day, just as surely as did Phases 1 and 2. The end might come when

---

* In 1978, in a *60 Minutes* report on car theft, an interview with a professional car thief concluded with this exchange—*Q:* How can one keep from having a car stolen? *A:* Don't get a car.

the nightmare of total blockage comes to pass—or with the exhaustion of fuel.

But some happier resolution might be possible. Phase 4 is definitely something to speculate about, as our view through the needle's eye shifts to the most important adjunct of car production: the fuel industry.

3

wwwwwwwwwwwwwwwwwwwwwwwwwwwwwwwwwwwwwwwww

THE SHIP THAT SHOULD
NEVER BE

A logo for the conglomerates might be the silhouette of a super-tanker beside the silhouette of an ordinary tanker, the kind we see going in and out of ports like New York and San Francisco. The relative scale of the two could be compared to the picture of the ordinary tanker with the silhouette of a lifeboat by its side. Surely no more eye-filling symbol could exist of the diversified corporations' basic premise: *to us the profits, to them the cost.*

Remember their *us* is our them; their *them* is us.

The first supertanker to plow into the public eye was the *Torrey Canyon*, which went aground in 1967 and spilled 29 million gallons of fuel a hundred miles northwest of Brest, France. The spill did the greatest damage on record up to that time. The damage was sustained by seacoasts and resorts and the life forms of sea and shore and air of France and Great Britain. And, of course, the livelihood of many people was affected.

The spill might have been expected to do great damage to one or more conglomerates: the insurance company, the ship-owner, the cargo owner. Probably, if any conglomerates *had* been affected, no more supertankers would have been built, and those in service might even have been scrapped. As it stands now, so many have been built that there is a glut on the supertanker market.[1] There is no information in the popular press that any has been scrapped—at least not intentionally.

A little more than ten years and nine French-coast oil spills later, on March 16, 1978, a supertanker was scrapped—unintentionally. The incident represented the greatest oil spill in history—up to this writing. When the *Amoco Cadiz* came apart in the middle, 68 million gallons, or 220,000 tons, of light Arabian crude oil were released, leading to the greatest mass kill of marine organisms ever recorded.[2] The impact on the ocean floor is still to be assessed, but on land it can be more easily measured. The spill occurred in an area that provides 80 percent of Europe's marine-derived pharmaceuticals, food, and fertilizer. Cleanup cost $400,000 a day, though the most effective work was apparently done by the two thousand farmers, fishermen, oystermen, and seaweed gatherers who worked, in addition to salvage pay, for their bare survival.

There is always the question of blame. Here, responsibility was hard to pinpoint. Should we blame the people responsible for the behemoth's condition because of engine failure? Blame the captain and the tugboat captain for wasting valuable time haggling over salvage price? Blame the French government for its failure to send two supertugs to the rescue? Or for not having any supertugs because ordinary tugs handled most ships— just not supertankers? Should we blame the same French government for not prohibiting dangerous close-to-shore routes when it knew these facts about supertankers: 1. that from the time the first was built, the hulls were discovered to be "weak at the weight," too weak to safely support their cargo,[3] and that erosion from seawater outside and oil and vibration within hastened normal metal fatigue to further weaken the hulls; 2. that a supertanker traveling at normal speed needs four miles to stop. Nonetheless, the French government put the blame for the catastrophe on "deficient international rules for tanker navigation and sloppy crews in flag-of-convenience ships." It was the Bretons who blamed "oil multinationals."[4]

If we agree that responsibility lies with the oil multinationals, the problem becomes one of finding where to pin the blame within them. On the shipbuilders, whose responsibility normally ends, like that of car builders, at the time of sale? Or the shipowners: men who keep so low a profile most of us don't know they exist—like supertanker mogul Daniel K. Ludwig, whose assets are estimated at $3 billion? On the companies that charter the supertankers a cruise at a time from the faceless owners? On the insurers, though usually the cargo is "self-insured" by the oil companies, which reimburse themselves?

If, as such pessimists as Jimmy Breslin report, "great oil slicks smother plankton, a body that causes one-third of the world's oxygen to be produced . . . oil causes seabeds to die and fish to disappear,"[5] then who's going to sue the self-insured oil companies for oxygen and seabed death?

Possibly we are looking for the wrong thing, thinking that if we find people who lose money in the spills we will find those at fault. Possibly some people do profit more than they lose in the oil spills. This seems unlikely, but the assumption must be checked out.

The press and media are always brimming with dire predictions of that inevitable day when our earth will run out of fossil fuel. Much of the material on fuel shortages comes directly from the advertisers and public-relations people of the energy corporations. We are urged to conserve every drop, and so to postpone that day when we are left shivering helplessly in the dark. We are urged to turn off pilot lights and insulate our houses.

It appears that the people so concerned with our welfare are, by cynical negligence, spilling into the sea enough fossil fuel for all the pilot lights in the world, and that they are doing this not one lesson-teaching time but many.

Although the marine oil spills are one source of loss of this precious and irreplaceable fuel due to negligence and irresponsibility, they are not the only such source and perhaps not even the greatest. The name Paul (Red) Adair did not become widely known until some days after one of the North Sea oil rigs blew, gushing fossil fuel into the sea at a rate and in a quantity that may have made the supertanker spills up to that time seem modest.

Efforts to stop the destructive loss of the precious fuel were front-page news for some days before Adair was mentioned. The first mention was rather casual. He had been called in as the most courageous and successful troubleshooter in a dangerous and accident-prone industry. In the first news stories the man appeared with a swagger. No problem. He knew many tricks, and if one did not work the next would. Still, several days passed before any of the tricks was tried. No secret was made of the reason for the delay. First, a bargain had to be struck. When agreement was finally reached between the company doing the developing and the troubleshooter, the terms were kept secret.

Oil continued to gush high into the air and into the North Sea. The secret treaty was arrived at, and Adair's first trick might have stopped the gusher, but the stopper was inserted upside down, and it gushed too. The man was no idle boaster, though, and his second trick worked. The unmeasured gush of oil was stopped, and the world had a new kind of Robin Hood with the superpowers at his mercy: to me the profit, to you the cost. Only, of course, to Adair the *you* was the conglomerates!

Since the capping of the North Sea gusher, Adair has been hopping in and out of the news regularly. On May 14, 1978, after the NFC Petroleum Corporation's Rig 12 in Walton, Texas, had blown poisonous fumes into the air for four days, Red Adair was called in and the rig was capped. Adair might have thanked the courts for this enhancement of his image. Earlier, the landowner had sued to prevent the drilling of Rig 12 because of the hazards, but the judge had accepted NFC's experts' testimony that the well could be drilled safely "provided every precaution was used."[6]

By June 20, 1978, Adair had been away from Texas, in Djakarta, for fifteen days battling one of history's worst gas fires. This one belonged to Mobil Oil and Petramina Oil Company, Indonesia's national oil cartel, which had hired Bechtel Corporation (who "builds anything anywhere" and generally on a cost-plus contract) to build a liquefied natural gas plant. Adair eventually got the fire under control by drilling two 11,000-foot wells to relieve the pressure. However, on September 11, when our government's showcase oil-storage facility at Hackberry, Louisiana, sent crude oil spewing aflame from its 7-million-barrel underground reservoir,[7] Adair was troubleshooting elsewhere. This time he was in Cambridge, Ohio, where one of Armstrong Drilling Company's wells had burst into flames 60 feet high, "the largest gas blowout in Ohio history." That one, said Adair, was "very serious, very dangerous, but posed no threat to the surrounding area."[8]

Meanwhile, a number of incidents of fuel loss had occurred outside the area of Adair's expertise. These were in the new realm of the supertank-car.

By 1968, after the supertankers had shipped quick profits to the seven companies that control the globe's total oil supply,[9] the companies, and possibly their related petrochemical fraternity, began to find ordinary tank railroad cars slow and profit-delaying. Hence, they developed the supertank-car. There was only one apparently impractical aspect to this new creation, and that was the condition of our nation's rails and rolling stock, which were unable to cope with its tremendous weight. The resulting instances of derailments, explosions, fires, poisonous emissions, deaths, and forced evacuations have become so frequent as to be almost commonplace. According to Senator Lawton Chiles (D. Fla.), explosions of chemical-laden rail-tank cars have in the past ten years caused $50 million in damages, injured 1,341 people, and killed 43.[10]

Here again the oil industry has been able to persuade judges that it can operate without hazard. It has persuaded all the powers of the government that its operations—from rig to ship to tank car to storage—are safe. The industry is presently engaged in a costly campaign to convince us all of the absolute safety of LNG, the most explosive but at the same time most profitable (for the oil companies) form of fuel.[11]

Yet the accidents continue to mount up. They occur at the very time the industry is singing to the public its constant refrain about the preciousness, the irreplaceableness, of oil; urging us to insulate our houses and turn off our pilot lights, to

conserve for our children's benefit. Meanwhile, the reck-
lessness with which the oil industry allows its product to be
handled, in the interest of the fast buck, can only be described
as wanton.

There were several veiled contradictions in the industry's
pleas and contentions. By 1979, storage facilities were filled to
overflowing. This glut had idled a third of the world's tankers
and cut the world's shipbuilding business in half.[12] In May
1978, the oil surplus had caused panic at the meeting of
OPEC, which decided the glut was too serious to justify its
usual price rise.

The sudden oil glut resulted when the world found itself to
be richer in oil than it had realized:[13] 1. Venezuela had announced that its Orinoco Basin oil reserves amounted to 700
billion barrels, at least double the reserves of Saudi Arabia; 2.
Alaska oil was pouring into the West Coast from Prudhoe Bay
at 1.2 million barrels a day; 3. California had stepped up oil
production; 4. Hong Kong had reported new oil and natural-
gas development in the South China Sea, in addition to China's
40-billion-barrel offshore reserve. But all this good news failed
to cheer the oil interests, who had had a sellers' market for so
many years that there had seemed no reason to expect a
change.

A surplus of the deflated American dollar in the oil-producing countries did not improve the situation. Indeed, the situation appeared to be a confluence of the circumstances that
classically lead to price cuts. Not for the ingenious fuel industry, however. In the United States, the world's biggest fuel
customer, the glut led, by the fall of 1979, to a price increase at
the gas pumps, approved by the president in spite of his infla-
tion-stopping policy of rejecting price and wage increases.

The price hike was reassuring for the oil industry, but not
reassuring enough. The industry also wanted "economic incentives to encourage refiners to renovate the West Coast refineries, which was never done when it knew the Alaska pipeline
was being built and would pour crude into those refineries."[14]
"It's a crazy situation," sighed one oil representative. "It's been

one big tangle of bungling and poor planning on the part of both government and the oil companies." And a Standard Oil economist said, "There's been a lot of plain horse trading going on."

The reason the companies gave for having to raise our prices for fuel is that while the West Coast was awash in crude oil, it was oil that did not refine well into the lead-free gasoline the government demanded be used in the new cars. Lead-free fuel must be made from oil from Arab countries; thus our oil has to be shipped east through the Canal to Gulf Coast refineries, or exported, and this is all very expensive. Happily for the poor, hard-pressed oil industry, it had been farsighted enough to reserve $300–$400 million in costs to consumers during the good years, which it was now able to pass on to us, strengthening the arguments for a price increase.

The puzzle is not entirely cleared up by the press reports from time to time on the progress of our Energy Department's claim against thirty-three oil companies for more than $1 billion in 1973 overcharges to the public. Still, it is heartening to know that in July 1979, Gulf Oil agreed to pay half of one of these claims, $42.2 million. The money will not reimburse the bilked motorists but will at least partially compensate the government for the cost of fighting the oil industry, which has both the troops and the experience to wage effective court battles.

☆

Children, when they feel unloved, misunderstood, sometimes have accidents. Maybe all these super oil spills, blowouts, and explosions of supertank-cars are the result of our lack of appreciation and love for our fuel industry. The sensibilities of the oil companies are hurt, and they are unable to take proper precautions with their equipment. They can't seem to plan ahead well enough to build or update refineries able to handle the crude they exerted so much pressure on government and voters to obtain via the Alaska pipeline.

We could start by loving that Alaska pipeline. It is a triumph of engineering, a return to that earlier period when American know-how was the finest in the world. But environmentalists, those impractical villains, have vigorously opposed the building of the pipeline from the time oil was discovered on the North Slope back in the sixties. They have protested the cost, the inevitable damage to wildlife, and the disruption to the life-styles of Eskimo and Indian populations. Environmentalists simply did not take into account the *real* necessity for the Alaska pipeline; they accepted with naive simple-mindedness the idea that it was built to transport U.S. fuel to U.S. consumers, to relieve our dependence on foreign oil.

Now the claim is being made that the crude oil found in Alaska does not compete in kind with imported crude because it cannot be refined into good, non-smog-producing motor fuel. Rather, the primary value of Alaskan crude is for heat, urgently needed in our midwestern and northeastern states, but not in the West. So the pipeline was built in the wrong direction. All this information had to be available before the start of the $7.7-billion pipeline (paid for by us, the taxpayers). The industry is rich in scientists and computers.

Interestingly enough, the pipeline may have saved us for a few years from serious recession or depression, and it certainly helped save us from putting an end to inflation. As the Vietnam War ended, our government was caught on the horns of a dilemma. The mood of the people made it clear that when the inevitable postwar recession set in, the society would not allow itself to be safely eased into either another war or even a massive war-posturing military buildup.

For a time, the space program helped. It siphoned off quantities of expert salary-earners, allowing countless engineers, electronics people, physicists, mathematicians, and other highly trained, work-disciplined, well-connected, and ambitious people to realize the American Dream. It compensated the military in large measure for the downplay of war-posturing, because space technology is closely related to missile technology as well as to spy technology. Much as the gladiatorial games served the Roman Empire during times of trouble, the space program provided us with a good show.

But the space program left a gap, because it did not provide much in the way of jobs for ambitious, upwardly mobile working people, who are the most articulate and vote-prone portion of our working force. The building of the Alaska pipeline filled this gap. It provided steady work at high wages to our blue-collar, hard-hat elite, allowing them to retain their conviction that the American Way still had room for them.

It might be well, then, to try to love our entire energy industry, which is made up of a number of separate conglomerates—conglomerates able to act in unison for common goals, conglomerates that reach into every oil-producing country in the world, with the possible (not the certain) exception of the socialist countries. These companies do not control merely most of the world's oil but also a great deal of its uranium. They also control much of our country's coal, other items like copper, and have close connections with the companies responsible for developing, storing, and transporting all these items, probably including those giant users: the utilities.

☆

One item reported by the United Press in December 1978 was headlined "Total Safety for LNG 'Impossible.' " It explained that liquefied natural gas (LNG) was natural gas cooled to extremely low temperatures until it turned liquid so that it could be contained and transported in much greater volume. At a Senate subcommittee hearing on this product, an executive of one of the country's largest gas companies, Max M. Levy, vice-president of Columbia LNG Corporation, conceded that LNG could explode with tremendous force when it hit water, for example, and that "absolute safety for LNG is impossible . . . but inconsistent with national goals and the public interest because safety questions must be weighed against risk of future gas shortage, risk of losing LNG supplies to foreign markets . . . dirtier air as a result of shifting from gas to coal."[15]

To date, LNG has an outstanding record: no disaster on sea or land has yet been reported. Still, what is true of supertankers is also true of LNG shipping and storage facilities: they age and deteriorate; mortality comes not only to human beings but to all their works. Metal fatigues; erosion and vibration weaken welds and joints. And human beings make errors.

On July 7, 1978, *The New York Times* had reported that Algonquin LNG, Inc., told the government that it was unable to estimate the number of fatalities that might occur if one of its large liquefied-gas trucks crashed. It had applied for a license to move as many as twenty-one truckloads daily along a 55-mile route that included sections of elevated highways over congested downtown neighborhoods in Boston and Providence, Rhode Island. But a still unreleased draft report by the General Accounting Office said that certain kinds of accidents at gas-storage facilities could result in tens of thousands of deaths. To date, the broadest public exposure to information about LNG has come from a Mike Wallace segment on the television program *60 Minutes* in 1978.

But rather than delving here into the complex question of LNG storage facilities near cities and earthquake faults—and the related question of nuclear-power plants similarly sited—it is worth turning from this complex and disagreeable subject and simply restating the apparent rule of conglomerates, including the fuel conglomerates: to us the profits, to you the cost.

☆

None of us will soon forget the fall and winter of 1979, when waiting, frustrated motorists shot each other in the long lines leading to the trickling gas pumps, and more self-controlled citizens quietly had heart attacks.

The waits for gas, frequently for the wrong kind for our engines, were symptoms of even deeper pain, of threats to the nation—symptoms of an undermining of our whole economy. Most of the people waiting and watching were convinced or suspicious that the shortages were not caused by the excuse given: the overthrow of the Shah of Iran, great and good friend of U.S. oil interests though he was.

Indications that our seventh postwar recession* was advancing had been troubling most of us for a variety of reasons: first of course, we have learned that recessions eat up jobs and businesses; we have also learned that from the time of the Great Depression, the manipulators of our economy have resorted to war, cold, hot, or both, as the quickest and most profitable way to reverse or at least arrest slides of the economy.

Had the economy been at its most robust, a long fuel shortage would have created serious strains, as we found out in 1973. Just by striking at the automotive industry, gas shortage threatens a sixth of our jobs.

In 1979 the automotive industry was in no condition to sustain such an attack. It had disregarded the lesson of 1973: that big cars are gas hogs and should be phased out except for special purposes.

The manufacturers have had a different viewpoint: big cars are not much more costly to produce than small cars, and can be sold at prices comparable with their size, so they manufacture handsome bottom lines.

Except for General Motors, the car people had persuaded themselves that they could keep our love affair with their big, beautiful product green. The error turned their ink from black to red. As the year wore on, Chrysler, already in trouble, faced bankruptcy, and the UAW accordingly faced the loss of many thousand union jobs, and called for either nationalization or national bail out. Chrysler got the bail out and lost $1 billion in the year, a loss that will probably fall heavily on the taxpayers. Ford Motor wobbled, and American Motors wheezed, but the oil companies, whose huge fortunes predated the age of the automobile, but had fattened on the automotive industry from its birth, went their merry way to the greatest profits in history.[16]

---

* A graph of the U.S. economy (*World Book Encyclopedia*, vol. D 5, p. 127) shows recessions since World War II in the following years: 1. 1946; 2. 1949; 3. 1953–54; 4. 1957–58; 5. 1960–61. Since printing, the sixth has been widely reported as occurring during 1974–75. The seventh began in 1979. The dates of post–World War II wars are: cold war, 1948; Korean War, 1950; aid to French in Indochinese War, 1953; start of Vietnam War, 1955, and then acceleration.

Their reaction to the proposal that they pay windfall taxes on their excessive profits to provide some relief for the burdened citizenry, and especially for the poor and old of the cold parts of the country who could not possibly warm themselves because of the inflated costs of fuel, was to advance two arguments that canceled each other out: 1. that they must have the profits for exploration of domestic oil, to make us self-sufficient; and 2. that most of their profits had been made not in the U.S., but abroad.

Unquestionably, they made vast profits abroad. There were three ways they must have done this: 1. by controlling foreign oil in order to sell it at a profit; 2. by selling oil either domestic or foreign outside the U.S. instead of within; and 3. by diversification—in other words, from businesses capitalized with oil profits, but business having little or nothing to do with oil or any other form of energy.

Those profits indicate they had oil they could have supplied to fill our needs. But their primary concern is neither petroleum nor patriotism.

Our new decade has begun with a lessened fuel shortage, but continuing rises in the price of oil. Inflation, largely triggered by fuel-price inflation, has reached 15.6 percent in the first month of 1980, and the specter of recession is still with us.

The role of big oil is therefore worth studying.

A large block of those windfall profits is being channeled into what may be the greatest advertising campaign in history. The press is awash in full-page ads explaining how those bumper profits are being used, all for the benefit of us—the American consumers, who should show our gratitude by paying two dollars a gallon without grousing, and while turning down our pilot lights. Television has also become saturated with similar commercials.

We who read and watch are the public. How convinced we are by this campaign that Big Oil is our big brother, is hard to estimate.

Convincing us may not actually be all that important to the

advertisers; the impact of those hundreds of thousands of petrodollars on the media and the press may be the primary purpose of this vast outlay (which after all is tax deductible as a business expense, to be sure).

Important then to look through the needle's eye at what changes are taking place in the media, changes that may have been triggered by that windfall of petrodollars.

Well, to find records of oil spills, blowouts, refinery explosions, or fires is not as easy today as it was in 1978. Then, there were pictures and feature stories, even on the front pages of our newspapers. Now, we have to comb the news with a fine-toothed comb. Spills, sinkings, and other avoidable waste of our valuable fossil fuels, and even of human life, are generally played down these days. Oh, they are there. The disasters have not gone away. Far from it. The collision on July 19, 1979, between the *Atlantic Empress* and the *Aegean Captain*, for example, resulted in an estimated loss of 150,000 tons of oil compared to the 223,000 lost by the *Amoco Cadiz* on March 16, 1978, yet press coverage for the 1979 disaster was modest.[17]

Are the media downplaying news that is important to our welfare?

Are petroadvertising profits affecting our opinion makers in other respects?

There has recently been a subtle and elaborate buildup of a climate receptive to the idea of imminent war—the buildup seems based on the premise that any old war is all right in a recession.

☆

Central to the theme of this book is the question of where princely chunks of big oil's superprofits are going.

They are not going for oil exploration, nor toward the purpose of making our country self-sufficient in energy production. They are going into mergers and diversification, into the building of the already mammoth and already diversified oil corporations into even greater entities.

When Exxon announced its intention of using a billion of its dollars to buy an electronics conglomerate, it explained in pious terms the close connection of the coveted company to the central problem of energy.[18] Exxon was not merely seeking a way to siphon off windfall profits before some of them would be earmarked for taxes. Oh, no. It wanted the electronics company because it had this valuable patent for an energy-saving device.

The regulatory agencies and even the courts vigorously protested this huge merger. But Exxon was sweetly reasonable. It promised, cross its heart, to divest the new giant acquisition of its energy-related component.

The merger went right ahead, but it did not remain the biggest for very long. The $3.65-billion merger of Belridge Oil and Shell, the largest corporate merger in history, was approved on December 10, 1979.[19] Next?

4

~~~~~~

LABOR-LEADER
CONGLOMERATES

"Greedy, corrupt, self-serving"—these words are often heard when the big-labor leaders are discussed, whether by union members, employers, or people outside both groups. Never mind whether the speakers are rich or poor, young or old, men or women, black or white, these words come out.

All the same, it took the president of the country's second biggest union to publicly blast his fellow leaders as fronts for the big employers. Douglas A. Fraser, president of the United Auto Workers, said, "The coalition of the country's top labor officials has become a useless façade to disguise a one-sided class war by business interests."

Fraser made this statement July 19, 1978, in resigning from the Labor Management Group, a semiofficial government agency set up to facilitate labor-management cooperation on inflation and other economic problems. This group was composed of big men in big unions, eight in all. George Meany, president, and Lane Kirkland, secretary-treasurer of the AFL-CIO, topped the list, followed by four of their union affiliates' representatives of steelworkers, textile-apparel workers, seafarers, and plumbers. Then came the Teamster delegate, and, until he resigned in disgust, Fraser.

The eight top management representatives were not named,

but presiding over the group was John T. Dunlop, former secretary of labor.

Maybe Fraser's blast was an act of simple political spite. He might have been on the outside of some squeeze play or other. Possibly it was a personal vendetta.

Or maybe it was the simple truth.

My *Webster's New World Dictionary* defines a labor union as "an association of workers to promote and protect the welfare, interests, and rights of its members, primarily by collective bargaining." If the union leaders have been doing the best possible job of complying with this definition, then Fraser was wrong.

Here are a few facts about our labor unions today:

Between 1970 and 1974, the number of union members in the southern states fell from 15.5 percent of the workforce to 13.9 percent of the workforce.[1] Overall union membership fell slightly less. The last official figure places current membership at 25 percent of the workforce. That's the combined figure for men and women in the workforce. Of the 11 million women working today, not 25 percent, but 10 percent, have associations to promote and protect their welfare, interests, and rights.

Today, then, three-quarters, or 75 percent, of our total national workforce is nonunion, and this in spite of the fact that a number of new sorts of salary- and wage-earners have been entering into unions in the past decade: officer workers; government workers, including some of the police and armed services personnel; and farmworkers. These new entries have by no means offset the loss of union jobs in the old, established unions.

Further, during this period of vast and increasing inflation, nonunion wages have been rising faster than union wages. This discrepancy is explained partly by the 15 percent increase in the minimum wage, which enables poverty-level workers not to keep up with inflation, but to lag less far behind. It is also explained by the term "ripple effect," which leads nonunion wages to increase a step or so above the minimum.[2]

George Cruikshank of New York's Morgan Guaranty Trust explained the "ripple effect" in an article on November 6, 1978, in the *Oakland Tribune*. He said:

> It is very significant that non-union wages are rising faster than union wages, because three-fourths of the nation's work force is non-union. . . .
>
> Certainly, the minimum wage is a factor in these non-union gains. The worker who is above the minimum wage goes to his boss and complains that he needs a raise, too . . . there isn't enough money to go around.

There must still be some need for unions, because on November 11, 1978, Labor Secretary Marshall said that more than 600,000 U.S. workers, though protected by federal wage and hour laws, were underpaid in fiscal 1978 by almost $129 million.[3] That means there was nobody out there to help them get their legal rights.

As for the general health and welfare of the workforce, in 1977 one out of four U.S. jobs was found to be hazardous, and fewer than 5 percent of all workplaces were found to have industrial-hygiene services designed to prevent or reduce the exposure of employees to hazardous substances, radiation, or excessive noise.[4]

Today, occupational health hazards are being investigated intensively. Most of the inquiry comes from investigative reporters, photojournalists, whistle-blowers, environmentalists —unions have not been in the forefront of efforts to save their members' lives.

☆

All the same, U.S. workers are the envy of the world. Our wages and fringe benefits are looked to wistfully by most of the wage-earners and unemployed of the sprawling Third World, and some of the developed countries, too.

The seeming contradiction hangs together. Unions have come to represent a labor elite, by now pretty much a privileged and hereditary class. Though nepotism is legislated against in most branches of the government, it is rampant in labor unions, and the best guarantee of a coveted union-membership card in our rapidly shrinking, automated industrial system is to be born into a union family, and to have been a boy baby.

Membership in this privileged class suggests that a rule we've seen elsewhere can be profitably followed here: "I scratch your back; you scratch mine." This is a rule that keeps the same union leaders in office year after year. These leaders safeguard their jobs and social positions by representing a shrinking but well-heeled membership.

In the early decades of the century when union memberships were growing, an adversary relationship existed between employers and labor. A seventy-two-hour week was not uncommon and a sixty-hour week was normal. As productivity increased through mechanization, the unions fought for and won shortened work weeks. Unions formed the spearhead of the thrust for fewer hours, and so for more jobs within the mechanized plants instead of just more profits for the owners. The ten-hour six-day week became by steps the eight-hour six-day week, then the eight-hour five-and-a-half-day week, and then the eight-hour five-day week.

At that point, the movement stopped—just when automation was hitting its stride and there was every reason to expect a further reduction in the work week, with, of course, no reduction in weekly pay, because there was no reduction in output or profit.

During the years when the union leaders took their responsibility "to protect the welfare, interests, and rights of union members" seriously, the right to jobs for a membership proportionate to a growing population was protected. Not so today. Shrinking job markets are taken for granted throughout almost every segment of labor represented by unions.

In those earlier days, most of the unions were "lily white" and male dominated. Minor changes have occurred in these areas, but the pressures for change have come from outside the unions, not from their leadership, and often not even from their submissive rank-and-file.

Pressures for minimum wages, child-labor laws, the right to organize, unemployment and disability insurance, worker's compensation, and pensions were also once strongly reinforced by the unions.

In short, during the years when the union movement was growing in this country, its leaders, organizers, and members were in the forefront of the struggle for those benefits we all have now whether union members or not.

Today unions are shrinking and so are their values. They are not concerned about the whole working force and the conditions of work; certainly not about the growing body of unemployed. At best, their concern is for their shrinking membership.

A retired "piecard," the union name for a privileged official, described his colleagues' attitude with astonishing honesty: "When we have our annual convention, the delegates who convene to represent all the nation's locals actually form a bigger body than the biggest local in the country. Naturally, then, we unite to put our own interests first: all *our* fringe benefits, and especially pension benefits. After we've looked out for ourselves—our biggest union local—then we get what crumbs we can for the rest of the locals."

Today Fraser's accusation may well be true: that the union leadership provides a façade for the big employers; that in effect the two groups are not sitting opposite each other at the negotiating table, but are on the same side, with the labor leaders fronting for the employers and safeguarding profits at the expense of the health and welfare of the people who do the work that makes the profits—and who pay the union dues.

Let us look through the needle's eye then, to see if it is possible that the big unions have grown so admiring of the conglomerates that they have turned themselves into labor conglomerates.

☆

In 1954, Edward R. Murrow interviewed George Meany. Meany was at that time, twenty-four years ago, the president of the American Federation of Labor, the biggest labor organization in the country, with its 110 affiliated unions. He was nearing the normal age for retirement. In the interview, he worked hard to project the image of a simple, folksy, Brooklyn-Irish plumber's-union advocate, living a simple, homey life with his stout, domestic wife, their greatest joy being visits from their grandchild.

The image was something of a double exposure. Meany's simple, folksy home was in suburban Washington, D.C., its spacious grounds overlooking the golf course on which the President of the United States played. An impressive bit of real estate.

He stated his union philosophy frankly: "When labor accepts the employers' right to make a profit, and the employers accept labor's right to make a decent living, then all our differences can be settled at the negotiating table."

The year after the interview, the AFL merged with the CIO, the Congress of Industrial Organizations, and Meany stayed on as president of this conglomerated union organization. It was not until October 1979 that he finally announced his retirement, turning over the reins to his hand-picked (and conglomerate-approved?) successor.

Let's refresh the memory. The characteristics that make a conglomerate are the merging of already large organizations, diversification among the components, and rationalization —that is, the pruning away of less profitable portions of component organizations in the interest of the bottom line, the profits of the shareholders.

The AFL-CIO fits the definition of a conglomerate better than it fits that of a labor union.

It was formed by the merging of two differently organized labor-union complexes, craft and shop unions. At first the unions were two large, politically powerful federations: the

AFL unions were organized by crafts; the CIO by shops. It is no coincidence that the marriage occurred during the McCarthy era, when all threats to the rising conglomerate structure were being labeled un-American and Communist.

When the two already merged federations rolled themselves into a ball, even greater diversification resulted than that within the biggest conglomerates. Here was a potential source of power that could easily counterbalance the power of the huge corporate structure. This power, wielded for its defined purpose, would have been great enough to halt labor's two great enemies: inflation and unemployment; to promote the growth, not the dwindling, of union membership; and certainly to protect the health and safety of its rank and file.

The union conglomerate did not do those things, but it did live up to the philosophy George Meany had stated honestly to Murrow: "accept the employers' right to make a profit, and the employers accept labor's right to make a decent living."

A drawback existed—clearly considered by Meany to be a minor one—that labor, in addition to accepting the employers' right to make a profit, had to accept a future with an ever-dwindling segment of labor making a decent living. And there was crow to be eaten for dessert: labor had to accept continuing inflation, which steadily inflated the employers' profits while it ate away at the income of the rest of the population.

With the merging of the AFL-CIO, Meany had under his thumb the greatest part of the unionized segment of what outgoing President Eisenhower knowingly named "the military-industrial complex." * With all this potential political power, Meany made no move to prevent the export of vast conglomerate profits to cheap-labor countries, or to cheap-labor, non-unionized parts of our country, though he could not help but realize those measures meant loss of jobs and weakening of unions.

---

* Remember, he had been commander-in-chief of the armed forces before he became president.

Not that labor was silent. Its voice was heard when certain kinds of jobs were threatened: the jobs of the union membership elite. It was especially vociferous when, along with the threat to such jobs, there was seen a parallel threat to the employers' right to make a profit. When there is any threat to the war industries—which, as we have seen, are generally believed to furnish a lot of jobs, but do create profits, taxes, deficits, and inflation—the voice of labor leadership is heard. It is also heard when environmentalists or consumer advocates propose long-range benefits to the country that threaten immediate conglomerate profits. Labor leadership speaks out not for the profits of course, but for the immediate jobs threatened, as a mannerly façade should speak.

So much for the AFL-CIO.

☆

Then, there are the Teamsters.

The Teamsters' Union is the largest in the country, but it has some of the built-in handicaps of a large single-industry corporation in competition with a powerful, diversified conglomerate. For all its size, it gets pushed into a corner. The big, big employers don't urgently need the collaboration of the Teamsters as long as they have the AFL-CIO in their pocket, so the Teamsters have had to look down the line. What they found were the second stringers, the organized-crime syndicates.

This branch of our conglomerate structure is comparatively small potatoes. It has only a few commodities to diversify with: drugs, sex, smuggling, gambling, and protection. While these commodities apparently have a high markup, they also involve high overhead, so it is doubtful that the bottom line of the syndicates puts them anywhere but on the bottom of the *Fortune* 500 list. But here there is no public access to hard figures, which may be why these enterprises are often referred to as "family" businesses.

In any case, the Teamsters' Union, big, rich, but in the vulnerable spot of a free or private enterprise in the world of the conglomerates, was compelled to do its merging with organized crime, and these operations were conducted on the same principle that Meany was following: reasonable profits for the employers; a decent living for the employees. But the Teamsters did not prove as deft at the negotiating tables as had Meany, and a good deal of the decent wages of the Teamster membership that had been set aside for disability and old-age pensions went down the syndicate drain.

So did a number of the Teamsters' Union leaders. It is hard to find any incident in our national history that conflicts more garishly with everything we value as civilized than the unsolved mystery of former Teamster president James Hoffa's disappearance, and the gruesome, persistent rumor that he went the way of former President Nixon's most unwanted papers: into a shredding machine. The very rumor implies not only a plunge into barbarity, but a coverup that must have called for some high-level stonewalling.[5]

The unfortunate Teamsters, big but still ruggedly individual and relatively undiversified, finding their efforts to merge with the syndicate less than gloriously profitable, turned to another big, rich, hard-nosed branch of the conglomerate structure: agribusiness. There, quietly, in the tradition of diplomacy by secret treaty, the Teamsters signed contracts with the big growers of California's conglomerated agribusiness. Here once more the Meany formula came into play: to the growers, reasonable profits; to Teamster organizers, reasonable pay. The growers needed the Teamsters, because a very old form of unionism had been born again in the United Farm Workers under the leadership of Cesar Chavez and Dolores Huerta. This union was advocating that some of the vast profits of agribusiness be used to bring the livelihood of farmworkers (who were for the most part living in the squalor of earlier times or other countries) somewhat closer to the American standard of living.

Again, the Teamsters were blocked in their effort to merge. The simple, plodding UFW had not only gained the backing of the conglomerated AFL-CIO, and the independent International Longshoremen's and Warehousemen's Union, it had gained the support of a substantial segment of the consumers, who engaged in specific, nationwide boycotts—a nonviolent profit-eating technique. The Teamsters have been obliged to yield, or at least go to ground, with only those agricultural workers engaged in processing or mechanized work remaining under their jurisdiction. Still, in the increasingly mechanized and conglomeratized industry that agribusiness is, this may prove a juicy plum for our biggest labor union.

☆

Recently there have been many indications that the 40-hour work week is lengthening for much of the white- and blue-collar elite.

Early in 1979, CBS aired a program called *Inside the Unions,* which dealt with rank-and-file members' attitudes toward their union leadership. The steelworkers who were interviewed went further than Fraser in their denunciations. One said, "We've got a leadership that's been in bed with the company"; another, "The people at the top ain't been in the mill for fifteen or twenty years. They're out of touch"; and another, "They can schedule you to work twelve hours a day, they can schedule you to work sixteen hours a day."

Further checking indicates that they can, and indeed they do. In these decades of increased automation, increased unemployment, and increased work stress, the strongest and ablest workers, those in the prime of life and productivity, habitually work considerably longer than from sun to sun.

Since overtime is paid at least time and a half, and much of it double time, putting top producers to work on extended schedules might seem to violate concern for the conglomerate profits. Not at all. The companies use this technique to cut back a substantial percentage of their payroll numbers. In this way, they save all those fringe benefits that were hard won in the militant days of the unions' past: unemployment and disability insurance, worker's compensation, Social Security, and pension funds.

Those are the direct, immediate benefits to the employers.

But other, less obvious benefits accrue to them as well. Those overtime workers—alert, vigorous, what school counselors might label "leader potentials"—earn impressive, very impressive, annual wages. They feel that they have good reason to be satisfied with their jobs, and are out of sympathy with their fellow workers who are unable or unwilling to make so great a commitment of time and energy.

Further, these bonanza wages establish family spending habits (partly to compensate for the sacrifices demanded of the family by the disruption and stress of the heavy schedules) and the resulting financial obligations create anxious dependence on the employers and a submissiveness to them.

A report in the *Los Angeles Times* on April 6, 1979, is worth thinking about from this viewpoint:

> One possible clue to A-Plant Error: maintenance technicians at the Three Mile Island nuclear power plant worked 40 consecutive days without a day off in the period immediately before the March 28 accident that officials now attribute in part to human error . . . and for all but three days before the accident, maintenance crews were working 10-hour shifts. . . . Spokesmen for Metropolitan Edison Co. refused to discuss personnel working hours . . . [and] "I am not aware of any rules applying to the number of hours a person can work," said Clare Miles, an NRC information specialist, "our regulations are related to the amount of radiation they can take." . . . The same crews had been working on both reactors, Three Mile Island I and II.

5

~~~~~~

THE TAXPAYERS' REVOLT

We called it the Taxpayers' Revolt, California Proposition 13, or the Jarvis-Gann Initiative, and most of us discussed little else after we discovered one afternoon that almost overnight more than 560,000 people had signed the petition that rocketed it onto our June 1978 ballot.

Here is what the proposition said:

> The maximum amount of any ad valorem tax on real property shall not exceed one percent (1%) of the full cash value of such property. . . . [Amendment added in November: "The full cash value base may reflect from year to year the inflationary rate not to exceed 2 percent for any given year."]
>
> Any change in State taxes enacted for the purpose of increasing revenues . . . must be imposed by an Act passed by not less than ⅔ of all members elected to each of the two houses . . . except that no new ad valorem taxes on real property . . . may be imposed.*
>
> . . . same requirements for cities, counties and special districts.

* An ad valorem tax is a tax or duty on the value of an article or thing subject to taxation.

Wherever I was, the people I heard discussing the initiative were arguing not with each other but with themselves. That was such a switch from the usual political discussion that it turned me into an avid listener, and that takes considerable turning.

It is important for me to explain whom I was listening to. If you define our economic and social system on an alphabetical scale from A to Z, the A, B, C groups are the first and second *Fortune* 500, the Jet Set, the Beautiful People. My contacts with them have been microscopic, and so have my contacts with X, Y, and Z—the people of the urban and rural slums who live in deep and basically hereditary privation.

By having begun myself in D, E, and F—groups who inherited or acquired property, stocks, taxes, and other generally agreeable problems—and sliding down the alphabet to U, V, and W, I have gained at least a social entry at the varied doors without really being able to claim a firm membership in any one specific group.

So it was that during the months-long pre-election discussions of the Jarvis-Gann Initiative, I had a range of friends, neighbors, relations, and working associates past and present spanning the scale from D to W to listen to. Not from one of them did I hear a clear-cut pro or con on Proposition 13. The division was not between one set of interests and another but within each of us and our conflict of interests and concerns. All agreed that something had to be done about the ever more burdensome tax load and the inefficiency of the bureaucracy, but we worried about what the cutbacks would actually cut. The focus of each self-debater's anxiety depended on his or her particular field of interests. D was worried about what would happen to the schools in general and her children's education in particular; E and family were active participants in cultural activities and so knew that inflation had already made inroads in library, museum, and performing-arts budgets. Continued inflation and then slashes in the budgets of valuable services—this seemed to be the way things worked.

F's deep interest in cultural matters was outweighed by social concern. Some financial clout would remain on the side of the museums and such, but considerably less would stay on behalf of mental-health programs and all the vast, intricate network of social services. Nowhere in the alphabetical social range did anyone show a complete lack of concern about some specific job or jobs, for self, friend, or relation. Yet in each stratum, balancing the concern over jobs was that over the rocketing cost of housing. Rents were soaring, since landlords used tax rises to justify raising rents. Similarly, increased tax rates were crushing homeowners, since assessed valuation went up each time a neighboring property sale took place in the ever rising market.

Ultimately the debate was resolved: Proposition 13 passed. And so the stage was set for tax rebellions in other states.

Proposition 13 did not pass in California because more rich people with property lived in the state than poor people with survival problems. It passed because the people caught in the middle—not rich or poor, but those who once could have been called "comfortable"—were so desperately squeezed by their tax burdens and so angry with the bureaucracy that they were able to persuade themselves that cutting back taxes would result in cutting the fat from government.

A good many years before the taxpayers' revolt took place, an old friend I had not seen for a long time crossed my path again. In the course of our catching up on mutual friends, work, developing interests, he pulled a clipping out of his wallet and read it to me. It was a column by economist Sylvia Porter on the subject of welfare. Porter listed the various estimated costs of all our American welfare services, federal, state, and local, public and private. She added up these costs and then divided the horrendous sum by the number of welfare recipients in the nation. The resulting amount paid directly to each recipient, according to her figures, would have been something on the order of $20,000.

Porter is a brilliant and honest economist, and she did not drop the subject on this note. She continued by estimating the number of welfare workers and other bureaucrats providing the services, and concluded that, were the need for welfare eliminated, more people would be thrown out of jobs than actually received welfare. Her overall conclusion: the society would not be able to absorb this great body of unemployed people, and thus the ex-welfare-workers would have to go on welfare.

This chance encounter with a new insight through the eye of Porter's economic needle helped start my slow mental processes along the new lines of thought and new ways of reading and listening to the news that led eventually to this book.

Porter's column had been witty, even whimsical, but the implication was thought-provoking: what would happen to our national economy if we were to suddenly so rationalize our government that we could cut the bureaucracy to the bone? It has been said that the federal bureaucracy is one of the two largest conglomerates in the world. At the last published report, 2.8 million people worked in the government's highly diversified components. That figure is exclusive of all the state and local bureaucracies.

I kept Porter's premise in mind as I listened hard to the swirling arguments about Proposition 13, before and after its passage. I hoped that some of the confusion about the relation of bureaucracy to the other conglomerates would show up clearly in the eye of my needle.

Back to the trusty dictionary:

> BUREAUCRACY 1. The administration of government through departments and subdivisions managed by sets of appointed officials following an inflexible routine. 2. The officials collectively. 3. Governmental officialism or inflexible routine: see also RED TAPE. 4. The concentration of authority in a complex structure of administrative bureaus.

BUREAUCRACY. Our dirty four-syllable word. The Free Speech Movement of the mid-sixties had taken all the steam out of our old four-letter words, but at least it had left us that one lung-filling expletive.

☆

Our American bureaucracy got off to a slow start. The Constitution made slight provisions for a militia and a tax-collecting agency, and Ben Franklin soon introduced the penny post, also known as the postal service. The government early saw the value of a merchant marine and the need for peace officers and some means of controlling newly acquired land. Congress, the White House, and the judiciary formed the bulk of our federal services.

Then came the Industrial Revolution. By the turn of the nineteenth century, democratic free enterprise was getting severely squeezed by the rising trusts and monopolies. In response to popular antitrust feeling, government bureaus were established to enforce new antitrust laws and regulate the railroads and the increasingly rich and ruthless fuel, food, metal, and banking interests.

Today, the populist parties and the radical right advocate a return to that time when free enterprise was unhampered by the interference of government bureaus. What most of these confused Americans overlook is that back in those days the trusts had already interfered with free enterprise and indeed squeezed much of it to death. The bureaus were set up to rescue what was left.

The problem was the trusts had already gained such vast amounts of wealth and power that they were able to regulate the regulators, and from then up to and including today, the tug of war has continued, with each side trying to strengthen its position. As we have seen, the trusts discovered that they could change their image by diversifying into conglomerates, and so grow bigger, richer, and more powerful than in the days when they were comparatively simple monopolies.

Suppose the taxpayers' revolt had won an ultimate victory, and all our bureaucracies—federal, state, and local—were cut to the bone. Where would all the bureaucrats go? Our bureaucrats constitute a bigger part of our working force than our unemployed workers, and they are voters. They are the children and grandchildren of immigrants to our democratic, free-enterprise Promised Land, whose parents and grandparents struggled to provide them with the education that opened the doors to opportunity. The ever dwindling ranks of private enterprise would be unable to absorb these people. And as for the conglomerates, their bottom-line demands have maximized rationalization; thus, as we have seen, whenever it is to the stockholders' interest, they export operations to countries with lower living standards and pay scales. There's no chance that they would absorb and gainfully employ the bureaucrats pared away from their jobs by popular demand.

That leaves one solution to this hypothetical problem. A great many foreign investors are exporting their capital from their countries to ours. Our ailing dollar offers them the promise of rationalizing their own operations and providing their stockholders with higher profits. Perhaps far-sighted investors are looking toward a time when a vast and desperate labor pool will be at hand.

Every political campaign in memory—local, state, and federal; right, left, and center—has shared one plank: the determination to improve government efficiency, thus cutting the bureaucracy and government spending. Always after an election a brief postvictory honeymoon publicizes a few photogenic economies: lights are turned off in the White House or thermostats turned down. Then new bureaus are established to regulate the bureaucrats.

Let's fantasize the possibility of a successful taxpayers' revolt. Let's imagine that the government suddenly began to run as cleanly and efficiently as a production line designed for profit and that all the people pared from the old tangle were securely employed in productive jobs. Would government then get on with the business of governing (that is, protecting the interests of the nation's citizens)?

Consider another source of interference with the governmental process, more insidious than the inefficiency of bureaucracy: We think of chief justices as pretty cool, precise types, but on Thursday, August 23, 1979, one was so stirred by righteous indignation that she scrambled two images and produced a verbal hybrid: "Once again, money will be the mother's milk of politicians with lobbyists owning the dairy," said California Chief Justice Rose Bird.

The president had referred to influence peddling, though less vividly, in the beginning of his State of the Union address of July 16; then he shied away from the ticklish subject. He had said that getting programs carried out in Washington was very difficult. "You see a Congress tugged and pulled in every direction by hundreds of well-financed and powerful special interests."

In their different ways, the two officials confirmed a statement by Federal Trade Commission Chairman Michael Pertschuk in his comments at a May 1979 seminar, who defined the problem more fully: [1]

> The fear is that these huge private enterprises, which are among the most tightly controlled organizations in our society, will increase their power at the expense of smaller and less organized groups, and of the individual. . . . The emergence of political activism as a first priority of the corporate manager . . . removes any shadow of a doubt that aggressive political activity has become not only respectable, but the hallmark of a corporate leader . . . enhancing the absolute political power of the merged firms.

Here we are, face to face once again with the conglomerates. The only questionable part of Pertschuk's fear is that he casts it in the future tense as a possibility instead of in the present tense as a matter of fact.

Alexis de Tocqueville, whose foreigner's-eye view of the United States inspired and distinguished his classic *Democracy in America*, seemed certain that power bargaining did *not* characterize our government in the 1830s:

> In democracies those who fix high salaries, being very numerous, have little chance of ever drawing them themselves . . . it must be admitted that democracy is excessively parsimonious only toward its principal agents.

In America officials of secondary rank are better paid than elsewhere, but high officials are much less well paid . . . this is clearly seen in the U.S., where salaries seem to diminish as the power of the recipients increase . . . in general, democracy gives little to the rulers and much to the ruled. The opposite occurs in aristocracies.

Today, by De Tocqueville's definition, our president is an aristocrat. As evidence, here are a few of the costs to the taxpayers of our presidency: salary of incumbent, $200,000; expense allowance, $50,000; "pension" for previous presidents, as well as for Gerald Ford for less than eighteen months of service (appointed, not elected), $100,000; expense account for previous presidents, $50,000; pension to former disgraced president, $90,000 to $100,000; expense accounts to same, $50,000. No doubt, unpublicized sums go to the widows of previous presidents.

Congressional salaries have also risen considerably since De Tocqueville's observation of democracy's stinginess to its public servants. Pay for congressmen, as of October 1979, was $60,663, with pension of $47,054 after three years' service.[2]

This is low compared to high industrial incomes. There are, however, many perquisites: special tax relief; free medical care; travel allowances; extensive paid staff; franking privileges; and the privilege of outside earnings.

A piquant congressional extra is its very own gas station, where on June 17, 1979, gas was still sixty-seven cents a gallon. Good service, convenient location, and no lines.

From a *Washington Post* article of June 7, 1979, published on page 6 of the *San Francisco Chronicle*, and titled "Washington's Most Exclusive Gas Station," we learn that in 1978 "the elite station's biggest customer was apparently House Speaker O'Neill. He used a total of $1,720 worth of gas and oil there . . . His limo cost taxpayers a total of $27,256 for the year."

On the whole, however, such presidential and congressional costs are probably a small part of the expenses of government that come out of our pockets.

The *Fortune* 500 gives a lot of information about our biggest industries. However, it does not tell what these industries pay out of their awesome combined assets of more than $1 trillion to influence the government and its many branches. As consumers or taxpayers or both, we pay all the costs of influence peddling by outright bribe or subtle pressure.

In recent years, campaign contributions have come to be overseen somewhat and direct bribes prevented at least in part, but many indirect but powerful pressures are still unregulated or only partly regulated. Examples include juicy posts in the private sector after service in the government, high salaries, and appointments of relatives of government officials to plum jobs.

Among former public officials whose knowledge, sympathies, and connections are valuable to the private sector, these are a very few: Richard Helms, former director of the Central Intelligence Agency and then ambassador to Iran. Helms, along with his international consulting firm, Safeer Company of Washington, was hired as a consultant by Bechtel Corporation, a tightly controlled company with one hundred projects in twenty-seven countries, including a $9-billion project in Saudi Arabia.[3] Helms joins other former public servants at Bechtel: former secretary of the Treasury George Shultz and former Health, Education, and Welfare secretary Caspar Weinberger.

The transitions sometimes have run the other way. John A. McCone had served as president of Bechtel before being appointed director of the CIA in 1961.

A glowing example of the value of governmental insight is William E. Simon, who was secretary of the Treasury under Nixon and Ford.[4] Mr. Simon now benefits from the enormous cachet a former Treasury secretary enjoys in American corporate life. In addition to serving on five prestigious boards, including those of Citibank and Citicorp, for an estimated $150,000 a year; he has his own consultancy firm, and three consultancies bring him an estimated $500,000 a year. He also manages his personal portfolio. Royalties of $200,000 from a book, A Time for Truth, were turned over to Lafayette College.

Now let's look back for a moment at our California Proposition 13, the Jarvis-Gann Initiative. What of this promise to the California individual, the homeowner or renter?

The initiative cut $7 billion from the state's property taxes. Of this, 24 percent benefited homeowners; 40 percent benefited owners of commercial, industrial, agricultural, and rental property.[5] By October 2, 1979, the California State Board of Equalization reported that property assessments in California rose 13.8 percent in the previous year,[6] almost equaling the Proposition 13 cut to homeowners. Such rises in assessments, for the most part, are due to the constant buying and selling in an inflated market. Commercial property holds steady or depreciates. There is little turnover.

Proposition 13 did benefit industry. Standard Oil of California saved $47 million in property taxes in the year; Wells Fargo & Company saved $1.2 million, which it gave to public television, housing rehabilitation, and the United Way as "a one-time grant, not an ongoing program."

The trigger for passage of the Jarvis-Gann Initiative was believed to be widespread protest against bureaucratic costs in general and the welfare program in particular. Welfare grants are largely funded by state and federal governments, so were not directly affected. But on March 6, 1980, the San Francisco Chronicle reported that cutbacks in consumer protection and watchdog services have resulted in increased welfare fraud.

Bureaucracy haters, however, were probably pleased to learn that 18,821 public servants had been laid off, and that most state and local government employees went through the year without pay raises.

The state managed to meet its expenses with the aid of $1.6 billion from the federal government and the rest from state bail-out funds.

There have been cutbacks in school programs, libraries, sewer maintenance, and public health programs.

There is the threat of an increased sales tax.

Did rents go down? Of course not. And what services were lost? Only those that affected individuals, very few that affected our corporate friends.

6

mwwwwwwwwwwwwwwwwwwwwwwwwwwwwwwwwwwwwwwwwwww

GARBAGE, SEWAGE, AND THE CONGLOMERATES

One of the first things I was surprised to learn when I moved back to a city big enough to have garbage pickup service was that just about the only bond uniting everybody and his dog was hatred for the garbage man.

They hate him for waking them up at dawn with noisy, smelly trucks—though that's the only time the big trucks can get through, since we clutter up the streets with traffic all the rest of the day. They hate him for smelling like garbage. Our garbage. Our smells.

Whatever he charges, they hate him for overcharging for the job they would not have at any price.

Not I. During all those long Depression years spent homesteading on a marginal Arizona ranch many miles from the nearest garbage service, I had sighed into my garbage many a morning, "If I ever have a garbage man again, I'll wake up every morning he comes around and smile."

We didn't use the word *recycle* then, but that's what we did. Every cull had to be divided by category. There were dog scraps and cat scraps, chicken feed, pig feed, an occasional treat for horse or cow, and then humus for my innovative humus pit, burnables for the wire incinerator in the corner of the yard, metals and other treasures for my husband's precious cannibalizing pile that with his ingenuity kept our few and essential decrepit pieces of equipment running; and finally those discards, accumulated until there were enough to truck to an arroyo for erosion control. (When I visited the old homestead a couple of years ago, I found my successor turned enthusiastic archeologist, excavating treasures from my very own kitchen midden.)

Our ranch recycling would enchant one of today's leisurely ecologists, but I did not have the leisure to spare for enchantment. Garbage took a confounded lot of time, most of it my time, since most of it fell in that bulging category of woman's work.

I used to think that, unlike the other tenants in my apartment building, I had hardly any garbage. *They* shopped at supermarkets and overbought, much of it convenience foods. *I* ate fresh meat, fruit, and vegetables, lived frugally, drank in moderation, cooked enthusiastically for a few friends every week or so, and cultivated my lifetime's accumulation of sales resistance.

I thought.

Until I got my exclusive garbage can in the basement, and discovered that most weeks I really had to crunch to get all my garbage stowed inside it. That took some thinking, some needle's-eye assessment of what I and my neighbors were paying to get hauled off every week. Then I began to think about our national garbage problem and to ask myself whether the conglomerates had anything to do with it.

I went back to looking at my own garbage. I shopped on foot, combining exercise and economy by limiting purchases to a reasonable load to lug up hill and stairs. When I unpacked the purchases, I seemed to have a bigger portion for the garbage can than for the refrigerator and storage cupboards.

Scientifically speaking, a week's study of my own garbage would not be a valid sampling. One 52nd of 1/220 millionth of the problem is not much on which to base the answer to the question: Is there a relation between that unspoken conglomerate creed—To us the profit, to them the cost—and my bulging garbage can?

That week, before I shopped I'd cleared out the refrigerator. For all my vaunted sales resistance and frugality, there had been quite a few items for the garbage can. Even with inflation the many tempting items displayed had led to overbuying.

Now I spread my week's purchases on the table, unwrapped the packaged items and put the packages in the garbage can (not directly, of course, but in the plastic bag with which I had lined the can, another of the many bits of petrochemical products that swell the garbage, along with wood pulp in the form of cardboard and paper products used for instant discard, materials we are asked to conserve because they are growing scarce).

The package of soap reminded me, as I unwrapped it, of a demonstration Andy Rooney had given at the end of a recent *60 Minutes*. He displayed a tableful of packages and he demonstrated that each of the packages had enough space to hold two of the items it contained. Rooney did not labor the point, but there it was. We spend a considerable share of our income on air; on pretty packaging that creates the illusion we are getting more than we are.

How much of our income? Wood pulp and oil might be rare and growing rarer, but the actual cost of the material in most of the packages is pennies or less.

We pay a lot more than pennies, because the design of the packages is a big and lucrative business.

On July 27, 1979, Joan Chatfield-Taylor had a full-page feature story on Walter Landor in the *San Francisco Chronicle*.

> If you have smoked a pack of Parliaments, eaten a Sara Lee coffee cake, drunk a bottle of Lite beer . . . your life has been touched by Walter Landor. . . .
>
> His activities go under a lot of names—package design, corporate identity programs, exhibit planning, marketing. . . .
>
> He understands the peculiar, conflicting American attitude toward business. We admire success, but we have doubts about bigness. . . . "We understand the emotional needs of people," and so well, too, that he can ask "a com-

pany to commit thousands and sometimes millions of dollars to a new look."

Those millions are not spent. They are invested. To fill our emotional needs with packaging that will first tempt us—and soon after, go into our garbage cans.

Papers, packages, petrochemical bags, wasted food, bottles, cans . . . and mail. A lot of mail goes into my trash can. Mailing lists are big business; because advertising and public relations are big business. Every dollar contributed to a worthy cause turns the spigot on a stream of solicitations, all mailed for nonprofit or for bulk-mail rates, except the many mailed under the frank by our public servants, reporting on their activities, and requesting our sage opinions.

Sometimes useless household appliances or raggedy garments go into my trash, but not in the quantity I see put out on the pavement by householders with children. Broken toys, shoddy appliances that looked fine on television and the variety-store shelves. So much profit-turning, built-in obsolescence. A lesson not entirely wasted on the kids.

Movements have for many years been afoot to treat garbage as a recyclable asset: either compressing the garbage into building material or tapping it for methane gas. To date, the chief products of these ideas have been expensive studies and more expensive pilot projects. These two forms of bureaucratic brain-recycling create some jobs and more taxes, but have not as yet proved a potential source of conglomerate profit, and so come to dead ends.

Meanwhile, the refuse accumulates in every community and creates massive and costly problems of finding more land for disposal. Land taken out of productive use, and off tax rolls.

As for sewage. The recent two-year drought in California brought home to many who had not thought about it before, how much of our sewage problem is an artificial problem. We Americans, in our average extended lifetimes, probably produce higher mountains of human waste than any other people ever has before us, and our exploding pet population contributes generously to the output. We and they eat more, and drink more, and much of what we eat and drink is programmed first for corporate profit, and then incidentally for our bodies, so our unprogrammed bodies slough off as much of it as possible.

Adding to the excrement in the sewers are all the water and cleaning material we use, as well as all the water and cleaning material we waste. It has been one of the conglomerates' earliest and still surest source of profits to make us as frightened of dirt as possible, including every simple biological function that can be twisted into an object of fear or disgust. The snake-oil barkers of Barnum's day used hope and faith to sell their cure-alls; ours use anxiety, fear, and disgust.

A surprising addition to the nation's sewage problem are the recent dumpings of our country's corrals, barns, stockyards, poultry farms. In the day when most of our food was produced on family farms, fertilizer from livestock and poultry was a valued addition to the farmer's income either directly from sale, or indirectly from soil enrichment.

Agribusiness has changed this. The priority of these conglomerates is immediate profit, so speed of operation and saving of labor costs is vital. On the vast acreage where once there were hundreds of family farms, manure is washed into the sewers and chemical fertilizers are sprayed or spread on the land—all in the interests of the shareholders. Old-fashioned farmers and organic-food nuts shake their heads. They note that natural fertilizers are not only better for the soil, but produce safer and better vitamins and nutrients than the chemical industry.

Apparently, the conglomerates have made such very tidy profits for their shareholders from my garbage and yours, that they have extended the principle on their usual gargantuan scale.

Skim your newspaper for a week and you will come up with modest items about some astonishing incident or other, from the grim tale of the Love Canal or the poisoning of an extensive ground-water system, to the astronomically costly and apparently insoluble problems of the safe disposal of radioactive waste.

Trace each incident back, not with violent anger but with cool examination, and you will see how two threads twist together: one is the conglomerate urgency for maximized profits for its shareholders, and for the merging of ever bigger and more powerful organizations—urgency that overrides ignorance or doubt about the safety of its products and the consequences of their fallout; the other is our own passivity. Let us not beat ourselves over the head with guilt because we have abdicated so much of our government, so much of our democratic power, to the ever growing money-power-control of the conglomerates. Guilt is just time and energy wasted. History— first the Industrial Revolution, then the present electronic one—frustrated many early attempts of wise and thoughtful people who struggled and are struggling to keep democratic control. Many attempts, not all. There is still time, just not much time to waste. The time we spend being intellectual and self-righteous and talking to ourselves about our problems is not entirely wasted, but it is not used to its best advantage.

Abe Lincoln said it: "You can fool all of the people some of the time, and some of the people all of the time, but you can't fool all the people all the time."

There have to be clear, simple, and reasonable answers to the ugly problems of our garbage and our sewage. All we have to do to find them is to stop letting the conglomerates fool so many of us so much of the time.

7

BUT GRANDMA, WHICH ONES ARE THE CONSUMERS?

We have been taking a surprised look together at the one visible institution that has grown from scratch during the same period that our problems have been worsening: the diversified, conglomerated corporation. While these corporations grew big and rich and powerful, they kept so low a profile we were hardly aware that an entirely new social and economic structure was in our midst.

Now, with a sense of the omnipresence of the conglomerates firmly settled in our minds, we can turn to face the problem most of us list first among our personal worries: inflation—and the variety of mental-health problems, depression, addiction, the many kinds of overconsumption, that might be related to it. Let us start with a riddle: How can inflation, which hurts almost all of us so much that most polls name it our most serious problem, worse than crime, profit the conglomerates?

We know that for the past thirty years—almost forty—inflation has continued with no reversals, and at an accelerating rate. This has been our country's first period of continuous inflation, but for conglomerates it has also been the period of almost unimaginable prosperity and growth. It must follow, logically and inevitably, that inflation has not hurt conglomerates, but has enriched them; indeed, inflation appears to be their life blood.

We are not going to explore the question of how the conglomerates manipulate this monstrous shell game of continuous
inflation. Our riddle deals with a somewhat simpler question:
how does inflation, which nibbles away at our dollars, profit the
conglomerates whose deals are all funded with dollars just like
ours?

Let's take a hypothetical, middle-sized, twenty-nine-unit diversified conglomerate and see how it operates. Literally
hundreds of real conglomerates could serve as examples here,
but in the interest of both fairness and simplicity, we'll use an
imaginary one. Every statement that follows could be verified
by a study of any conglomerate's annual reports, or even by a
close study of the news items that appear over a period of time
about any one particular conglomerate.

Here, then, is Conglomerate X, an average-sized conglomerate, so low on the *Fortune* 500 list that it feels the breath of the
Fortune Second 500 hot on the back of its corporate neck. Its
worth is listed on the stock exchange at $Y billion, the ag-
gregate worth of its piddling twenty-nine diversified holdings.
For simplicity's sake, let's call Conglomerate X's chief executive officer Mr. X. Mr. X has an information pipeline to our
government in Washington. If he did not, or if he were to lose
it, Conglomerate X's board of directors would rapidly replace
him. As an important financier he must know the news before
it happens, and he does. (If he were CEO of a bigger and
richer conglomerate, he might make it happen, but we are
using a middle-of-the-road organization for our study.)

Most of us might guess that since inflation has continued for
almost forty years it will continue into the coming year, but a
guess is not good enough for Mr. X. He must know, and he
does.

He also knows that inflation benefits borrowers. Most of us
understand the relation between credit and inflation in a general way. We know that lenders lose from inflation. If I lend
you five dollars today, I am lending the worth of a little five-
dollar sack of groceries, but if you wait a year to repay me, and

inflation has risen 10 percent, then you will be paying me back a smaller four-dollar-and-fifty-cent bag of groceries.

This principle hits us hardest in our savings accounts and pension plans, because the money we put away for rainy days and old age in past years does not offer much help any longer, and promises mighty little for our retirement.

So we realize that the converse must be true: in times of inflation, borrow money. The more you borrow, the more you profit from the diminished worth of the loan.

Mr. X knows this, too, and he has watched closely the prime practitioners of this principle.

His role models, the giants who tower above the run-of-the-mill multimillionaires like himself, are the executives whose organizations "can boast that they are in hock for $3 billion"—which are AT&T, Exxon, Mobil, Sears, ITT, General Telephone, and Dow Chemical.[1]

Since, in an era of ever continuing inflation, it is sound business practice to owe money, the more a conglomerate is able to owe, the bigger its profits and the sounder its financial rating.

This is very hard for us low- and middle-income taxpayers to understand. We know that when our debts go over a certain percentage of our income, the 18 percent per annum carrying charges we have to pay on each credit card and charge account pushes us to the wall. Logical to expect that the interest alone on debts of $3 billion would bankrupt even the wealthiest conglomerate.

Instead, it lays the foundation for bigger mergers and acquisitions. Of course, conglomerates do not pay 18 percent per annum interest as most of us do. It made headlines when the prime rate—their rate—went to the historic peak of 15.5 percent in November 1979.

G. I. Williams, Dow's chief financial officer, explained debt benefits at the 1979 annual meeting. The company earned $363 million before taxes on the money it had borrowed, with interest of $287 million, and all of that tax-deductible.[2]

Now, Mr. X has been seriously considering acquiring Corporation Z, which has a profit potential but needs rationalizing (remember, that means streamlining the operation, preferably by cutting back the payroll, or enlarging the operation so much that it will cut back the competitors' payrolls).

With a borrowed $20 million, Conglomerate X acquires its thirtieth diversified moneymaker, and Industry Z becomes just a thirtieth of the activities Mr. X must devote himself to in this inflating quarter. He must also oversee his twenty-nine other diversified projects. All twenty-nine started the year in good form, since the two that had made only modest profits the previous year had been divested. Mr. X's credit is fine, and the mere $20-million loan for an acquisition, far from extending it, has increased it. So he borrows all the money he needs to stockpile supplies and raw material for most of his operations, knowing that inflation is on his side in these loans too, and will work for his profit. Moreover, sensible Mr. X knows that his friendly government will not compel him to peg his selling prices to the preinflation costs. Of course, with this dreadful inflation, Mr. X must pass price increases on to us even though his suppliers were not fast enough to pass them on to him.

"But wait," you say, and you are right, "a lot of those products Mr. X needs are controlled by other conglomerates, and they are not willing to release them for his profit when they can hang on for their own."

Mr. X has several choices for dealing with those corporations in his stable that are threatened with this kind of conglomerate gouge. Let's say that his Unit 19 is a candy factory. Inflation has dealt a double whammy to the price of sugar, Unit 19's vital ingredient. Sugar's inflated value has risen far higher than the good old profit-making 2 percent planned upon for this quarter; sugar is up 5 percent. No chance of stockpiling. Quite the opposite. The conglomerates that control the sugar market are the ones stockpiling. Mr. X's Unit 19 must either buy at a premium or close the plants.

Poor Mr. X. Here he is confronted with the same inflationary problems as the rest of us.

We-e-e-l-l, not exactly the same. Several roads are open to

him. First, he can raise the price of his candy bar. Second, he can put a smaller candy bar in the same-size wrapper, and thus satisfy the consumer by not raising the price. Third, he can do both.

But maybe he is not willing to invest in the retooling and public-relations expenses that any of these three solutions might entail. He still has a lot of options. He can merge with one of the conglomerates that has a sugar-producing or sugar-marketing component, either by mutual consent, or by one of those mysterious raids that make reading the financial section of the newspaper so exciting. The principle is simple; the practice is so complicated that it is making a whole new class of professionals rich and sought after: merger specialists in law, banking, accounting, scouting, and public relations.

Each of us has observed the principle of merger in practice, either at first or second hand. I did, when my son went to a new high school after we moved from a small town to a city. He had no friends, but did have a paper route. Then he met up with an older boy who had no paper route but did have a switchblade. A merger was indicated, and the boy with the knife acquired an interim interest in the paper route. When conglomerates are successful in applying the principle, the merger is for keeps.

Thus, merging or acquiring a source of the principal ingredient is one way to beat inflation in this particular one-thirtieth of this particular conglomerate. The attempt does not always work. Raiders do sometimes have to back down, as American Express did when it tried to forcibly acquire McGraw-Hill Corporation; as Branscan of Canada, Ltd., did when it tried to merge with a reluctant F. W. Woolworth empire. In that kind of fix, it might be wise for Mr. X to move Unit 19 to another country, where even our inflated dollars command a buyer's market.

Indeed, whatever our dollar does in the inflation line, Mr. X has his finger on the pulse of all the countries in the world—all that might be of use to one or more of his thirty units.

If none of the foregoing options promises Mr. X the best

profit potential on Unit 19, then of course he will divest. This choice might seem to be a gloomy one: divestiture into a depressed market. But the option would not necessarily represent a misfortune for Mr. X.

First, there is the possibility that a sugar-producing or -marketing conglomerate might have been eying Unit 19, and might be willing to make a favorable trade or an otherwise reasonable deal. Then again, Mr. X might not find this possibility. Too many sugar users might be crowding the market. Take courage, Mr. X, help is at hand. Large numbers of foreign investors with cheap dollars are eager to buy into our nation's industries.

Many hard-pressed American businesspeople, tempted to sell out to foreign investors, hesitate when they remember our not always creditable record as investors in foreign countries, our cynical use of political corruption and indifference to public welfare.

Mr. X spares himself this sentimental consideration. It is his *duty* to place the welfare—meaning the profit—of his stockholders at the head of his list of priorities; a duty his colleagues and board members frequently remind him of.

So he has the option to divest himself of Unit 19, and in a deal that is not the least disadvantageous to his conglomerate, regardless of inflation. He can sell to a foreign investor who has a lot of cheap American dollars to invest.

"Hold on, there," he might find himself reflecting, debating with himself about the offer he is considering from Herr Omar-San. "That candy unit is a pretty reliable, over-the-years profit maker." A lengthy consultation with his accountants is in order, and the conclusion is very likely to be that in spite of the inflated cost of sugar, the problem of how to avoid raising the price or lowering the profit can be solved by reduction in the size of the candy bar—too slight to require serious retooling or an enlarged advertising campaign. Unit 19 will remain in the black.

There are two more effects of inflation that may work to the benefit of Unit 19. The first is the time lag between rises in sales prices and rises in wages and salaries. Suppose Unit 19 is still located in union territory and the union contracts under which the several plants of Unit 19 operate were signed two years ago for a three-year period. A cost-of-living clause in each contract probably provides up to a 5 percent annual raise, in case of continued inflation for the current year. The contract might have been reached after amiable negotiations, and with no conflict. Or it might have been protested angrily by processors and public as greedy and inflation producing—15 percent in just three years, 5 percent a year or $X million for the industry. Let us say that since the signing of such a union contract two years before, inflation had advanced 15 percent or 7.5 percent a year. The company would have made a 2.5 percent annual profit on wages. And let us say that for this third year Washington had whispered that the inflation rate would go well above 8 percent, giving at least another profitable 3 percent on wages to the stockholders.

Even with a moderate margin on a middle-sized payroll of an average-sized conglomerate, the time lag between inflation and cost-of-living pay increases spells conglomerate Profit with a capital P. In non-union country the principle applies for minimum-wage hikes.

Now let's look at the final advantage inflation gives the conglomerates. This advantage hurts fewer of the rest of us than the pay-price inequity, but those of us who are hurt are damaged grievously.

The advantage is that inflation bears down heavily on small- and middle-sized businesses, just the people we think of when we think of the free-enterprise system and the American Dream. Here is the group many of us hope to join some self-employed day in the future, so we can get out of the conglomerate rat race. It is this small, shrinking group that the conglomerates seem to take the most heartfelt pleasure in squeezing out of existence.

Competing with other conglomerates in each particular field is part of the game that CEOs play with such gusto that many hate to retire. As Pauline G. Hollis recently reported in the

San Francisco Chronicle, "No one keeps track of such things nationally, but in California, statistics show . . . of the 100 largest industrial companies . . . 30 percent of the chairmen and presidents are 65 years old or more, and 15 percent are over 70."[3] This game is played much like polo or horseracing, with a set of rules, among members of the same clubs and golf clubs and patrons of the same hotels and restaurants, so that even losing to such respectable competition is no disgrace.

Small-business competitors don't even know the rules. They are quite likely to maintain so high a standard for their product that its quality undercuts the market; or they might resist inflation so strongly that instead of profiting by it, they pull in their belts and hold the line for price and product size. Simply not sporting. They might even be so ignorant of the principle of rationalization that they give pay raises that keep up with inflation, instead of lagging behind, and so produce some disaffection among conglomerate staff.

Mr. X is a kind and decent man. He is sincerely sorry that inflation is hard on pensioners and on young people starting out in family life. He regrets that it creates so many problems for schools, hospitals, cultural organizations, and sundry other services. His regret is not strong enough to induce him to lobby to control inflation, but still, he is sympathetic. So sympathetic that he makes many generous contributions to those pinched and worthy causes: his dear old college, the opera, the Salvation Army, a museum, a library, a medical research fund. These donations are all tax deductible of course, so very tax deductible that if he is generous enough he can slide his income right down to a lower tax bracket and save money. Another nice feature of Mr. X's private benevolence is that it makes it possible for the tax attorneys who have helped him with these economies to find a perfectly legal way to apply their considerable charges to one of his conglomerate units as a business expense.

Mr. X never asks his attorneys to find ways to help his free-enterprise competitors escape the squeeze of inflation. No indeed. Any legal advice he might seek here relates either to acquiring them—cheap, for an added inflation bonus, or to squeezing them out of business, preferably safely into bankruptcy.

The 1978 figure of $1.2 trillion for five hundred conglomerates already cited tells simply and clearly that conglomerates ride triumphantly on the crest of inflation like expert surfers in choice surf, while the figures on bankruptcy, liquidation, and sellouts to conglomerates of independent enterprises tell what inflation does to the group politicians like to refer to as the backbone of our democratic system. Beatrice A. Fitzpatrick, director of the American Women's Economic Development Corporation, says four out of five new businesses fail over a five-year period; the failure rate for new business ventures by women is probably higher.[4]

In the year of this writing, with foreseeable and foreseen accelerating inflation in each quarter, all but two of Mr. X's closely watched components are doing well. As we've seen, Unit 19 has problems. Unit 13 is faced with a different problem—it is violating pollution standards, and the time granted by the Environmental Protection Agency for solving the problem is running out. Unless the proper bureaucrats in the EPA consent to another delay in plant modification, Unit 13 must either invest several million dollars in minimal modification, pay a fine for violating the government emission standards, or move the plant to another country. Mr. X will present the cogent argument that this dreadful inflation would make the capital investment a hardship for the stockholders at this time, and that therefore, unless the EPA grants another extension, it will be necessary to close down the plant and export Unit 13 to a country without an EPA.

It is clear from this rather commonplace incident that conglomerates behave in no way like those militants and terrorists who hijack planes or seize hostages to impose political blackmail. Legally, logically, and patriotically, Mr. X makes it clear that continued pollution serves the national interest, because closure of the plant that creates it would cause mounting unemployment and add to our welfare and unemployment costs.

The Congressmen representing Unit 13's home base will probably be supportive of Mr. X's position.

In any case, fortunately for Mr. X, there are plenty of countries available with all the requirements for Unit 13: minimal pollution standards; large, cheap labor pools; and inflation rates so much greater than ours that our dollar hardly seems at all inflated by comparison.

☆

I had puzzled over and finally reasoned out the way that inflation, which causes me and my friends serious problems, was turned to profit by the conglomerates.

"Simple!" I exclaimed. "Our problem is that we don't owe enough," and I took my "plastic money," also known as "silly money" or "Chinese money," and went first on a buying spree and then on a vacation.

It didn't work. Delightful memories, of course, but the bills kept coming in, and I could not learn the conglomerate secret of keeping the principal and just paying back the interest (tax deductible).

All my monthly bills showed that my spending limit was pretty well used up, and that my unpaid balances carried compounded interest of 18 percent a year, or, put more kindly: 1.5 percent a month, which sounds very low. And each bill had an enticing bargain offer attached to the payment envelope— which could of course be charged to the account.

I had joined the credit club, but only as an honorary member. With my modest Social Security, a part-time job, and no dependents, I climbed out of debt and stayed out, but the experience offered valuable insight into how inflation hurts almost everybody outside the conglomerate hierarchies.

We are a troubled nation, there is no question but that we are. If there are 220 million of us now, chances are 200 million are beset by financial and emotional problems.

Inflation has made it possible for the conglomerates to prosper, grow, merge, diversify, and to pour out an unending stream of seductive, dazzling goods and services before our enamored eyes.

Most of the lure comes to us over the air, during those five hours of daily television watching that are the national average for every man, woman, and child. From the sets in our homes come a baffling variety of switched signals. Part truth, part lies: dangled temptations of objects so easy to buy, so hard to pay for, the obsolescence that will make them discards already built in.

The wish, the human wish, to believe what we are told, and the gut knowledge that we can't, carries over from the air to family, to school, to government.

I have referred before to the Russian behavioral scientist Pavlov and his experiments with dogs.

Think of the many switched signals not unlike those Pavlov used with the dogs, among which each of us live, and marvel that so many of us are partly sane.

Inflation is one of the master switches. Few of us keep close tabs on financial news, on the exact increases day after day placed on one set of products or another. We are joyously aware, though, the minute we get a bigger paycheck. The signal a raise sends out to us is: "We're better off: here's more money to pay bills or buy something we need or want. Or we can give a present, or put the extra money in our savings." So there's that 5 percent pay raise. First off, though it does not immediately register, the 5 percent represents the *gross* increase. Often, a raise puts our pay over a line into a higher tax bracket, and if this imposes 2 percent more income tax it lowers our pay raise from 5 percent to 3 percent. (Unfortunately, the conglomerates have better tax lawyers and get better tax legislation than we do.)[5]

Suppose two members of my family are working now and that our income is reasonably comfortable. A 5 percent pay raise for both members would seem to add up to a lot of happiness: less family friction over expenses, less anxiety about bills. No excuse now for not managing well, not saving more, pulling our lives together.

But inflation is like the tide, an incoming tide. It does not crash ashore and pull that 5 percent right out to sea. It moves in, percent by percent, with this higher price and that increased charge, and we are not actually aware at what moment the tide has risen 5 percent and floated our increase away. Who has the time, as the inflation tide continues to rise, to sit down, even with a pocket calculator, and figure out just how much it is necessary to cut our budget back, and how and where, to keep our feet dry?

So, for those who belong to one of the more fortunate groups, such as families with two incomes that raise the family income above the poverty level, inflation brings constant, nagging confusion. We are richer, and yet we are poorer. It doesn't make sense.

That's bad enough. Even young, healthy people, happy in work and in family, reach a certain stage where distrust, disharmony, anger, violence, often even the physical sicknesses of stress—heart attacks, asthma, insomnia, pain, proneness to accidents—begin to appear in the household.

Now suppose jobs are threatened or lost? And since America has become a shrinking workplace, it is crazy to be completely secure in any job.

Everybody knows at least from hearsay about the Great Depression. Still, though the early 1930s were terrible years, with 25 percent unemployment, the stress of those hungry times was not the stress of conflicting signals. Unemployment did not bring inflation, but its opposite, deflation. If you had a dollar you could buy a lot.

Today, in spite of constant talk about the wisdom of letting unemployment rise to make inflation lower, we all know the talk is twaddle. We have both inflation and unemployment, and both fluctuate only in degree. Neither has gone down except briefly or statistically during most of our lifetimes.

Today's highest officially admitted rate of unemployment is 25 percent among our young black American population—the rate, remember, that brought us to the brink of revolution in the thirties, a crisis that was probably averted by the New Deal and World War II. That is the highest rate, but not the only high unemployment rate. All our nation's youth, each ethnic and social minority group, our women, and our people caught between the prime of life and the age of retirement have high rates of unemployment—and just the same rate of inflation as the rest of us. Correction: the cost of necessities always rises above the general rate of inflation, because necessities command a sellers' market. So the lower our income, the higher our rate of inflation.

A problem that worries most of us more than we are willing to admit, but probably enough to produce a lot of stress, anxiety, and mental suffering in many of us, is this: if a national unemployment rate brought the nation to the brink of revolution in the 1930s, then how close to the brink of violent insurrection are all the pockets, urban and rural, of 25 percent unemployment today?

As we ask, we must keep in mind that the constant inflationary rise is right in there, driving these masses of mostly young, able-bodied, unemployed people to despair.

No wonder that drug traffic is said to be our nation's third most profitable industry,[6] that alcoholism, gambling, prostitution, and pornography are big business. In 1978, we had the cruel statistics of 19,000 murders and 28,000 suicides, with fatalities in vehicles or by fire greater than the two previous figures combined—so many of these unnecessary deaths triggered by alcohol, drugs, depression, or rage. Then pile on top of them all the stress-related sicknesses—heart attacks, high blood pressure, and the frightening number and variety of mental diseases.

Add them up, and we've got a mess on our hands.

This mess, looked at through my needle's eye, is undermining the quality of our lives because we have allowed an elaborate network of people to grow up in our midst who are delighted to view 220 million of us, the American people, not as people at all, but as consumers. I think we are still people.

It is the conglomerates who have turned themselves into the real consumers, voraciously vying with each other to see who can consume the most of us to feed themselves, their board members, and that group known as the Shareholders, who have come to evoke the pious homage traditionally paid to Motherhood and the Flag.

As a matter of fact the majority of the Shareholders, the small shareholders, are not actually part of the conglomerates, but are ourselves and our friends and relatives and neighbors: regular people, who don't really understand what the conglomerates and the huge shareholders are about.

At first view, it seems grossly unfair to say that the conglomerates are consuming our nation, our inalienable rights to life, liberty, and the pursuit of happiness. To do so is to credit them with a singleminded pursuit of their inflated profits at the expense of our land, our air, our water, and our people.

Look closely and carefully, please, if you find it hard to think so badly about a group of respectable businesspeople, to believe that they do not hesitate to consume our well-being. The simple truth is that they do not hesitate to consume each other.

"Merger mania" is the term financial reporters give the wave of business activity that began in the fifties, lulled briefly after court action was taken against the biggest conglomerate, ITT, in the sixties, and then flared with renewed and continuing violence through the seventies. Conglomerates are raiding, absorbing, and merging with each other in a frenzy that appears to be insatiable. No merger satisfies the hunger for power, it just whets the appetite for more mergers and greater profits. Subsidiary companies with sales and profits that prosperous middle-class businessmen would be proud of are divested because they do not satisfy the chief executive officers' inflated standard of profit.

The result is greater power in fewer hands, greater wealth and greater political power than that held by any previous aristocracy in history. This leaves 65 percent of us convinced that since only the interests of the aristocracy are represented on the ballots, it is useless to vote.

What this does to our future, and to our national security, will be looked at through the needle's eye in the next two chapters.

8

〰〰〰〰〰〰〰〰〰〰〰〰〰〰〰〰〰〰〰〰〰〰〰〰〰

THE LONELY OLD

In my first year or so back in the city, I saw San Francisco's big population of old people only out of the corner of my eye. I was driving my own car then (I don't anymore) and keeping house for my two high-school-age children in a neighborhood made up of students, lower-echelon staff workers at the nearby University of California Medical School, and those minority families who had managed to escape the deep ghettos. Many of the latter, I learned soon after I moved in, had been pushed out by the city's slum-clearance plan, which had sounded so good when I read about it in Sonoma County.

Soon I was invited to join a local photojournalist group. I was impressed by their exhibit at the Annual San Francisco Art Festival showing the impact on my neighborhood of this same redevelopment project. So I joined, and we went to work on the group's project for the next year's Art Festival: Old Age in San Francisco.

The city government and various organizations had become acutely aware that the voting population was growing older and older. Young and middle-aged, middle- and upper-income families were moving to the suburbs and the country. The city was quickly being left with the very rich, in their own delightful ghettos: the very poor—and the old.

Politicians, welfare groups, and special-interest groups had proposed and initiated a number of programs and projects for the old—oops, never the *old*, that word was taboo—for its "senior citizens." Senior-citizen centers were established in most neighborhoods to provide a sense of community, activities of interest, and services to the o— to the senior citizens. These centers resulted in a form of segregation, entirely new, as far as I know, to our species: segregation by age.

The theme of our group's show on the city's old people was "Don't just sit there, do something," and we photographed all the delightful things our seniors could do in San Francisco—with other seniors—and contrasted these admirable activities with the evils of passive noncreativity. I thought the show was unintentionally amusing, but it won a prize at the art exhibit. Besides illustrating activities made available at the centers, the show held up two role models to our seniors: Imogen Cunningham and Winifred Jobe, a photographer and a dance instructor, respectively. These were old people whom the city was justly proud of. The exhibit focused on their activities, which had started in each case long ago, when each woman was very young and feeling the burgeoning of much talent, and was continued throughout long and successful careers. To contrast with our portraits of these two women, we showed sitters on park benches, a rear view of an old man walking a bulldog, and two aging Middle European housewives engaged in an animated street-corner discussion.

I privately thought that park-bench sitting, dog walking, and animated discussion were all more creative than the senior-center activities we illustrated, which revived memories of cub-scout-den-mother and Bluebird-leader projects I did not mind forgetting.

With one exception, our group's view of the city's old and their problems was middle-class, conservative, and evasive. The exception was a stunning photograph—wish it had been mine—of the lobby of a Tenderloin hotel seen through its front window. It showed a scattered row of lonely lobby sitters. The face of a man in the foreground, facing toward the window but not looking out, said it all: the loneliness, the bitterness, the pain of pinched old age.

The next year my children grew up and flitted off, and my little car and I gave each other up, so I went back to the means of locomotion I had not used since my school days: public transportation. Soon I was riding with gloomy forebodings. Alone, my middle age fast going down the drain, I was confronted on every bus ride with the old, the maimed, the ailing, going on their halting, almost always lonely way, with or without canes, crutches, walkers, inching across the streets timidly or too often with suicidal indifference. Many had lines of pain in face and body, and more showed some reflection of that ultimate emptiness of the face I had seen in the lobby-window masterpiece.

And their smell, the smell of the old. Some of the urine stench that invades so many bus and trolley rides could be traced to a wino or two, but not many of the winos are old, they don't last that long. More comes from the sober, sick old people, especially the men, who have lost more than sphincter control—they have lost the hope or incentive of acceptance in the human family.

I soon learned that many of the not-yet-old shared my sorrow at the image of the lonely old. Perhaps it was this sorrow, this concern that led us to select our photographic theme. Each of us tries to somehow inch away from a sense of personal guilt: why can't I make more time in my busy life to visit my old relative or my old friend, who is one of the lonely old and who would be anyway a shade less lonely, at least briefly, if I could bring a little human warmth and interest into her or his life?

Maybe the answer is to give a little time to volunteer work, to doing good among the lonely old. Yet whatever I do is a tiny prick of light in a dark, gloomy netherworld—and a tiny easing of my conscience.

Or, instead of volunteer work, how about making a study of geriatrics? Technically, the word applies to the branch of medical science that deals with the physical problems of aging, but these days we use it loosely to cover the social, economic, and emotional problems of the aged, and sometimes just to avoid the words *old, aged, aging.*

Now I am a card-carrying senior citizen myself, so any problems I might have are problems of geriatrics. That means that, to students and problem solvers, I belong to a subspecies of the human family.

All right then. Time to look through my needle's eye at the problems of the aged. Are these problems, too, affected by the conglomerates?

☆

The chemical conglomerates boast often and long of their enrichment of our old age, our improved chance of longevity and prolonged youthfulness through the use of their products.

The tables on which insurance underwriters base their life-insurance premium rates are not quite so optimistic. Ours is probably the country with the highest average consumption of pharmaceuticals, but we do not have the longest average life expectancy in the world. Still, we might correctly boast the largest population of people with geriatric problems: problems of economy over a forty-year continuous period of inflation; acute housing, health-care, nutrition, and transportation problems; and lacing through the whole, the terrible problem of loneliness.

Of course, loneliness is not a problem on which the old have a monopoly. The Beatles song "Eleanor Rigby" is a classic of our time. Yet, whenever, in spite of our efforts to look away from it, we catch a glimpse of the terrible loneliness of the old; whenever we feel ourselves looking down an endless avenue of mirrors in which over and over and over again is reflected the look of hopeless abandonment, the almost unrelieved expression of the old men and women clinging to life but waiting for death in all the skid-row flophouses, the Tenderloin hotels, the retirement homes and retirement communities, the hospitals, the condominiums and elegant hotel lobbies, the assigned corners in the homes of children or hopeful heirs, each of us has to struggle against the gut-gripping fear: there is the second-to-last stopping place on my road.

Why is it that in this era, and in our country, we have for the first time in the history of man, massive segregation by age? What has happened to our whole social structure that has caused it to squeeze the old people out from the social body?

Look through my needle's eye at some of the root causes. First there is the breakup of families and communities. It has long been recognized that large corporations deliberately break up living patterns. The built-in, apparently compulsive, need to demand an overriding loyalty to the company leads to constant transfers of individuals, geographical and social, in either promotion or demotion; to constant moving of whole plants or factories or office complexes; and then to the moving of staff from one to the other of these, like pawns on a chessboard.

There appears to be a need to make the family subordinate to the corporation. The employee must yield to the employer's decision, so spouse and children must yield too, or break the family. In a small city I once visited that was dominated by a giant chemical complex, I learned that the corporate need for acquiescence dictated the rising young executives' choice of neighborhood, church, and clubs and imposed a social conformity that forbade divorce or scandal. Probably an extreme example of the loss of individual power to exercise our nationally treasured freedom of choice. Extreme in degree; not exceptional in kind.

Whole communities were uprooted by the enormously profitable war industries that preceded World War II and thrived during the war. The game continues. When I was young, San Francisco had a long tradition as a blue-collar town. Blue-collar workers, in early days called mechanics, are long gone. Industry, including our merchant marine, emigrated, and today San Francisco is a "paper city." Its employees, of whom I am one, work in banks and offices, primarily insurance offices, in high-rise buildings erected, as the saying goes, by corporations for corporations, and not by people for people, since people, without the prod of stockholders, would not have erected high-rises on the San Andreas fault, and would plan better uses of space and transportation than corporations seem capable of planning.

Some blue-collar workers are still needed in San Francisco to serve the office workers, the old, the very rich and the very poor who now make up the bulk of the population. They must compete for decent housing and living conditions with the businesspeople and their staffs, and this competition, aggravated by inflation, pushes them to "greedy" demands.

With all these moves of people like chessmen, the groups that suffer most are the very young and the very old.

The deliberate inflation so profitable to the conglomerates imposes a heavy burden on the aged. To be as sociable a human being in 1979 as I was in 1978 is 13 percent harder, if I subtract my small Social Security increase. The squeeze has gone on now for more than thirty years, and there is no light at the end of this tunnel.

There was a program on *60 Minutes* in 1978 that showed both sides of a power play between parents who needed housing and retired, prosperous senior citizens who demanded the right to live peaceful lives in childless apartment houses. The needs of both groups were clearly and honestly stated. The parents needed shelter for themselves and their children. The aged needed peace and serenity, to enjoy the fruit of their labor. Some of the labor had been the rearing of their own children.

Two points were not made. One, that there is something basically wrong with a materially rich society that cannot provide decent housing for all its people; the other is also an indictment of our conglomerate-dominated society: the fact that our children are hard to live around and old people are unable to adapt to younger people. Neither of these conditions are normal, healthy human conditions. They are both the result of abnormal, unhealthy social stress that has shattered our society into fragments of lonely, unadaptable, antisocial beings.

Since the days of the earliest hominids, people have lived in clans or groups and always with an integration of ages, and this social structure has continued through history in every country, in every social class. The social patterns that created societies, civilizations, cultures, were age-integrated societies in which the old were loving nurturers, warm companions, role models for the young. But in our own day we find packs of kids roaming like predators, preying on the old and the infirm; and ever growing communities of the old, communities vulnerable to adult predators as well who prey upon them in adult and more or less legal ways.

Pity the old, imprisoned by fear in rooms or apartments, but give thought, too, to the young whose rage is so tragically misdirected, but who have reason enough for their rage. "What are our chances?" they may be asking. "What kind of a world are those old people making for us to look forward to?"

9

wwwwwwwwwwwwwwwwwwwwwwwwwwwwwwwww

THE WINDS OF WAR

The gale forces of war that tear through our lives, sweeping us along like a flurry of autumn leaves, cast no shadow. Like navigators and farmers and scientists who must learn to turn away from the shadowless wind and look to the sky and the sea, we must look all about us until we can identify the forces that have the power to whirl us all into bloody contention with other human beings.

Again, our search must start with simple questions: Who loses from wars? And who gains?

The answers to the first are clear and visible: the people who die in wars lose. And their survivors, their mourners. And the ones who are crippled in body or mind. And their victims—"victims" of those who are themselves victims, losers. Finally, if it is true, as the arms merchants admit, that in peacetime a third of our tax dollars go for the tools of war, we all lose.[1]

Yet reason tells us this cannot be so. If we were all losers in war we would unite to end wars, but we do not do this.

Clearly, some of us must not only profit from war, but profit greatly.

"That record is cracked," the reader says. "You're going to blame it all on those poor conglomerates. Now you want us to think them monsters who manipulate us into wars for their profits."

Be calm. I'm not trying to pin all the blame on the conglom-erates. Let's review the situation without anger, restricting our view to our own country and the time within the memory of most of its people, the contemporaries of the atom bomb and the children born since.

This time begins at the end of World War II. First we en-joyed postwar prosperity. All during the war years people had struggled along with old cars, old housing, old everything. The slogan had been, "Use it up, wear it out. Make it do, or do without." When the war ended, there was a great gap to fill. Men and women were coming home from the wars, eager to establish homes and families and to enjoy the good things of ci-vilian life.

Thus began the baby boom and the housing boom. Con-sumption of meat, sweets, alcohol—consumption of everything soared. So did inflation. But then, there were jobs for all or al-most all (except ethnic minorities, who weren't counted much then, though there were even some jobs for them). Wages and salaries were the highest in history. And so were profits! But not everyone made money. The bigger the business, the bigger the profit—this fact of life was putting a squeeze on free en-terprise, on family farms and small enterprises of every sort. The era of mergers and diversification was in full swing.

And then came recession.[2] The specter of the still-remem-bered Depression (it had not completely disappeared until the prelude to World War II had brought demand for arms sales) stared businesspeople and workers in the face.

But not for long. Almost overnight, the cold war had started. Our ally of a few months back, the Soviet Union, was now the greatest threat to our nation. We turned now to build our recent enemies, especially West Germany and Japan, into our Chinese Wall against Russia. Within it, we began to bend all forces to arm ourselves.

Employment rose again. So did profits. And inflation. But the teeter-totter lost momentum, and again recession threat-ened.[3]

Aha! The Korean War.

That old phrase "peace and prosperity" had become out-dated. "War and prosperity" or "peace and recession" seemed the alternatives.

Prosperity indeed. This was Korean War prosperity: its in-gredients were continued inflation, even higher average in-comes, low unemployment, high profits, and an ever greater bulge of merged and diversified businesses buying out—squeezing out—free enterprise in agriculture, manufacturing, and merchandising.

A teeter-totter rises just so high above its fulcrum and then starts down. We began to feel recession. Inflation did not re-cede, but jobs did. Small enterprises went to the wall.

But everything was all right. There was our gallant ally, France, fighting a war in Indochina. Money and war matériel went from our country to aid France. The flow continued until her final defeat, on two fronts, Dien Bien Phu and the French home front.

Too bad for our country. Acting as suppliers rather than par-ticipants had been a good solution to the problem of recession. This role resulted in jobs for most and profits, vast profits, for many—and no sacrifice of life or limb, that is, of American life or limb.

We found other brushfire wars to supply around the world, and of course we had our own brushfires here at home: riots, police forces, National Guard, the continuing draft, all gen-erated jobs and money. And maintaining our dozens of out-posts around the globe as well as building up and modernizing our national defenses kept money moving through the econ-omy.

Too bad that all those markets just weren't enough without that big, juicy, munitions-expending Indochinese war.

First, a few civilian advisers were sent to those defeated allies of France, the free Vietnamese. Then military advisers were sent. Next, soldiers went, and more soldiers, arms and more arms. Eventually, this flow was developed into the great-est outpouring of military weaponry in history—more than had been used up to that time in all the wars ever.

It worked. Of course it did. Oh, sure, we lost the war. But look at all the jobs. All that inflation. All those profits. All those mergers.

Besides the killed, maimed Vietnamese and Cambodians and their devastated lands, the only people who lost were some tens of thousands of killed or wounded young Americans. Also victimized were a considerable percentage of our private enterprises, which sold out or were squeezed out by inflation, high taxes, and the tough competition of the prospering diversified corporations now calling themselves and being called conglomerates.

Trouble was, thousands of stupid, unpatriotic kids around the country began to lock arms and chant, "Hell, no, we won't go." And eventually that simple, viable system, the draft,* ever at hand to take care of those totters of our teeter-totter, those inflations, became a casualty of war.

So there we were. Things looked pretty hopeless, no? No draft. And the probability of safely plunging into another distant war diminished. Worse still, there was talk of recession and even depression.

At this writing we have a man in the White House elected on a platform of peace. But if you review that portion of our history with which this book deals—from 1945, the end of World War II, to early 1980—it becomes clear that it has not mattered a bit whether we had a man of peace or a man of war in the White House, a dove or a hawk.

Traditionally, the Democratic Party stands for small business and working people. It is the party of the majority, and tradi-

---

*The first U.S. peacetime draft *ever* had been initiated in 1940, with war clouds gathering in Europe and Asia. All previous drafts had ended on the cessation of war. Not so the draft of 1940. Without publicity or public debate, and certainly without a vote, the draft was kept on the books after the surrenders of Germany, Italy, and Japan. Its unpopularity, however, forced President Johnson's withdrawal from public life, and it ended January 27, 1973, the same day that the United States signed a peace agreement with the two Vietnams.

At this writing, 1980 has begun with a strong, and strongly resisted, movement to reinstitute peacetime draft registration of all eighteen- and nineteen-year-olds, probably both women and men.

tionally the majority wants peace, not war, which it is traditionally called upon to do the fighting of.

Traditionally, the Republican Party is the party of big business, the minority party, and the party most willing to take a firm hawkish stand in the name of national defense.

Now look at the sequence in the White House. When World War II ended in Europe we had a Democrat at the helm, Harry Truman. Thus, it was a Democratic White House that ordered the dropping of atomic bombs on two cities of Japan, our already defeated adversary.

Naturally, recession followed the end of the war, but was stopped in its tracks. Our Democratic president ordered troops into Korea. This White House also initiated the cold war, reinforced by the Truman Doctrine, the Marshall Plan, and the North Atlantic Treaty Organization. This president also sent thirty-five military advisers to Vietnam and agreed to provide the South Vietnamese with military and civilian aid.

For some reason, the majority of us did not elect another Democrat to carry out these policies.

We next voted a Republican administration into office: Dwight D. Eisenhower as president, and Richard M. Nixon as vice-president. Eisenhower had been supreme commander of the allied forces during our participation in the war, and commander of the NATO forces later.

Still, the general was elected on the promise that he would "bring the boys home from Korea," a promise he kept not immediately, but eventually.

In his administration we shouldered three-fourths of the cost of the French war in Indochina, and increased our contingent of "military advisers" in Vietnam. The cold war reached its peak during his and Nixon's administration with the era of McCarthyism.

At this time preparations were made for an invasion of Cuba, with the expectation that the invasion would take place under Eisenhower's chosen successor, Nixon. However, our voters apparently thought it was the Democrats' turn, and elected John F. Kennedy. This did not prevent the Bay of Pigs invasion, but might have weakened it. If so, this was the only change in defense policy that the change of party in the White House brought about. The unsuccessful invasion attempt was followed by the Cuban Missile Crisis, in which this Democratic White House led us to the brink of World War Final.

Military and civilian support of the South Vietnamese was also greatly increased under this Democratic administration, with policies that did not change after Kennedy's assassination and the continuation of the Democratic administration under Lyndon Johnson. Johnson's tenure intensified our military involvement in Vietnam, a policy so widely unpopular that it ended his political career.

Then it was the Republicans' turn again, and Richard Nixon was elected. Under his administration the already gross and bloated war was stepped up, with the expenditure of more money for weaponry than had been used in all the other wars in history. The war was extended (secretly) to Cambodia.

All the same, it was this Republican, hawkish president who "brought the boys home from Vietnam."

When scandal, which had forced Vice-President Agnew's resignation, then forced Nixon's, Gerald Ford entered the White House and continued the arms race.

To put exact dates on the record of the United States as the arms merchant of the world will probably be hard for future historians, because there is a rationale for secrecy in all matters connected with national defense. I will not deny the future historians their opportunity.

Instead, just review the situation at the time of the last election before this writing: that of 1976. The Democratic contender, Jimmy Carter, advanced these planks and won the election: opposition to the B-1 bomber, the most costly of all the costly Pentagon proposals; the promise to exert all efforts in support of strategic arms limitation—"I am particularly concerned," he said, "by our nation's role as the world's leading arms salesman. If I become president, I will work . . . to reduce the commerce in weapons."[4] He also promised that no new weapons would be developed at all for this unsanctified trade. What dealing was done would be from the nation's stockpile. And he opposed the dangerous plutonium-based breeder reactors with their production of nuclear-bomb material tempting to militants.

Some of these presidents had been elected with my vote, because I had been one of the 35 percent who conscientiously exercised my democratic obligation and privilege. In our hearts we knew it did not matter a fig which candidate was elected. In our hearts we knew the unfortunate incumbent in the White House, whatever his political party, would soon find himself a puppet, manipulated by unseen hands—regardless of what good intentions and honorable goals he started with.

The irony is that our invisible powers do not crave war and the destruction of the world. Not at all. Their concern is merely profit. They do not wish to atomize the old people and children of our nation or any other; they only want to provide the best possible return on their shareholders' investments, and the surest way they see to accomplish this is to step in with a war—hot or cold—whenever a recession threatens. Maximum profits need a sellers' market, and a sellers' market must not allow itself to become saturated.

With most consumer goods there is a saturation point. This can be pushed off by built-in obsolescence, but it cannot be entirely eliminated.

With goods for an arms race there is no saturation point, because the race creates its own obsolescence. Weapons become obsolete soon after—or even before—they leave the drawing board. A whispered rumor of a better weapon on the competitor's drawing board is all that is needed. Examine the last years of this race.

A step-by-step account of the first gradual and then not so gradual stepup of our arms race can be gleaned from yards of newsprint. Some bottom-line figures will serve as examples.

The nation's defense budget for 1978–1979 was passed with only slight modifications of the administration's slight modifications. "It gives something to everybody," said a report of August 5, 1978.[5] "Provides $36.9 billion for military procurement, which is only a fraction of the $119.4 billion of military appropriations, including salaries, defense operations, and programs."

This military-procurement bill, though the year 1978–1979 was peacetime, was the largest in our history. It was larger than the military-procurement budget for any year during any of our recent wars: World War I, World War II, the Korean War, the cold war, or the Vietnam War. Earlier wars, of course, are not even worth considering, fiscally speaking. They (the Revolutionary War, the Civil War, and so on) were fought with peanuts.

Our national deficit during the same year, to which this military-procurement budget contributes its share, was also the biggest in our history. Estimates vary as the dollar fluctuates.

Might one hope that, given this huge program for our own military procurement, the invisible powers might be willing to cooperate with the White House commitment to cut back our trade in arms for export? Between 1970 and 1976, our foreign arms trade had risen from $1 billion a year to $12 billion. In May 1977, an administration spokesperson, reiterating a promise to cut arms sales considerably, estimated our total worldwide arms trade to be $20 billion.[6]

Later, a new method of calculating our arms exports was inaugurated. Under this program, we now exclude arms sold to eight countries: the five NATO nations plus Japan, Australia, and New Zealand. Also, we no longer designate such items as jeeps and tents military items; rather, they are listed as "commercial." And sales of military equipment by private dealers, though they must be licensed by the government, are not included in the government figures.

With those various exclusions, Defense Department officials estimated our government-to-government sales in 1978 at $14.5 billion. Senate Foreign Relations Committee experts and Brookings Institution specialists set it higher: $16.5 billion plus.[7]

Then, there is the matter of the Strategic Arms Limitation Treaty. Defense Secretary Harold Brown told the Commonwealth Club in San Francisco, "You can be sure that no [SALT] agreement will be signed that is not entirely favorable to our country." Such a statement from one on the decision-making level raises this question: What does the Defense Department consider entirely favorable to our country, particularly at a time when we are troubled by the specter of recession or depression?

The answer, of course, is jobs. So let's look at jobs and the arms business.

Let's start with an item about the Lawrence Livermore Laboratory. Located in one of the most fertile agricultural valleys of California, the Lab, as it is affectionately known in Livermore, had in 1978 a monthly payroll of $10 million for its 6,600 employees. Its annual budget that year was $119.6 billion. The Lab is the think tank for the H-bomb, our most awesome deterrent weapon. It thinks about some other problems too, such as designing cheap fusion energy with giant magnets and lasers, but bomb thoughts are its staple.

In 1950, Livermore had a population of four thousand, and the area produced only chunky beef and classy wine. Now its population has risen to fifty thousand. [8]

"Sure it's a controversial place," said Mayor Helen Tirsell, whose husband works at the Lab. And, said Martha Dixon, winery worker, whose father-in-law is a Lab worker, "It's kind of a scary place and it makes you wonder what's going on there. . . . But maybe if we knew, we'd be even more worried. And whatever it is, it doesn't have any effect on the grapes." Chamber of Commerce Manager John Strong wrapped it up: "A $10 million monthly payroll. That's a great piece of industry out there." *

---

* What does go on at Livermore? On September 26, 1977, it was described in a *San Francisco Chronicle* report as the nuclear bomb "think tank" where "bombs are designed, not assembled" . . . but guarded anyway by the fourth largest police force in northern California. On January 24, 1980, when an earthquake occurred only ten miles from Livermore, the story changed somewhat. After the first shock (measuring 5.5 on the Richter scale), the laboratory announced that "leakage from a 30,000-gallon tank holding a mixture of water and radioactive tritium was reduced to a trickle by Friday

By looking at Livermore's $120 million payroll and realizing what the accumulated payrolls of our weapons industry mean in terms of jobs, it is possible to understand what the decision makers think might be a favorable strategic arms limitation agreement for our country at a time when the country is threatened with recession or, as is now being hinted in whispers, depression.

In 1975, a study by the U.S. Department of Labor reported that every $1 billion of foreign deliveries of military sales equipment required the employment of about 51,900 American workers—about one out of every twenty new jobs.

This estimate has been pretty well confirmed by Undersecretary of Labor Lucy Wilson Benson, who has cited more than seven hundred thousand jobs as being directly connected with foreign military sales.*

More than twelve hundred American companies are involved in these jobs: General Electric, Westinghouse, AT&T, Texas Instruments, and the Singer (sewing machine) Company are among the top twenty-five. The export of military equipment represents from 30 to 50 percent of all our total military business.

If there are seven hundred thousand jobs involved in 30 percent of the country's total military business, we can make a rough guess as to the number involved in the domestic arms, or defense, business. We can't get an exact figure, because the information is of course classified in the interests of national security.

Besides, Reuters reported that the Pentagon had invited re-

afternoon. Only 50 gallons leaked out." Apparently the tank involved was not the "think tank" in the earlier story.

*The statements regarding effects of arms manufacture on U.S. employment were quoted July 30, 1978 by James McCartney in the *San Francisco Examiner* ("President Claims Otherwise: U.S. Arms Sales Highest Ever," p. 1). By 1979, however, the International Association of Machinists' Department of Public Relations reported a loss of 12,000 jobs in their unions since 1975, due to automation of military production (*The Impact of Military Spending on the Machinists' Union*, by Marion Anderson, Washington, D.C., January 1979).

porters to see a new, energy-saving incinerator in action at the Pentagon.[9] "The incinerator burns ten tons of classified material daily and now supplies nearly 25 percent of the heat for steam and hot water in the Pentagon building," a Defense Department spokesperson said. Military secrets can now be turned into usable steam and hot water. It might be hard to estimate the number of jobs represented by that steam and hot water. Or the number of conglomerates that make a substantial percentage of their net profits from those military secrets. Or even the number of bureaucratic jobs also dependent—not very indirectly—on military moneymaking.

We can see now what the defense budget means to the nation's economy, but what does it mean in terms of national security to each of the citizens who pay for it?

Most of us are obliged at some time or other to entrust something we value to the charge of another person or group of people. The thing to be entrusted might be a child, a home, an inheritance. We look for certain qualities in the persons we choose to be responsible: honesty, dependability, loyalty, and, if possible, intelligence.

But here we are, entrusting the safety of our country, and, by extension, the earth, to a body of people who control enough weapons to destroy the earth forty times over.

☆

On November 10, 1979, United Press reported the following from Washington. The brief item, on page 6 of my daily paper, was modestly captioned "A Scare at the Pentagon."

> The American early warning system signaled a hostile missile attack on the nation yesterday, sending ten fighters into the air before the Pentagon determined it was a false alarm.
>
> The State Department said the false alarm was set off by a test tape run through a computer of the North American Defense Command. The tape simulated a missile attack.

"Through a possible mechanical malfunction the tape transmitted to other commands and agencies," the Pentagon said.

Officials caught the error within six minutes, but during that time ten fighter aircraft took off.

Neither President Carter, Defense Secretary Harold Brown nor General David Jones, chairman of the Joint Chiefs of Staff, was notified. Middle-level officials determined the alert was not the real thing.

The Pentagon declined to give more details of the alert, saying, "We do not believe we should provide potential adversaries with knowledge of our alert procedures by going into any great detail."

The difference between this incident and the climax of that filmic masterpiece of black humor *Dr. Strangelove* is that the Pentagon was given six minutes in which to recall its ten fighters with their nuclear warheads. This time.

Ten minutes instead of six, and the unwritten law of the conglomerates—"to us the profit, to them (meaning you and me) the cost"—might have been washed out. After years of reaping massive profits from war, the conglomerates too would have been presented with the bill.

10

vvvvvvvvvvvvvvvvvvvvvvvvvvvvvvvvvvvvvvvvvvvvvvvvvvvvv

OUR NATIVE BENT

Alexis de Tocqueville, step forth from the pages of your *Democracy in America*. We need you. Remember, when you visited our shores in 1830, our republic was just over half a century old. And when your ship docked after its long, slow sail from your native France, you needed no needle's eye to examine our smaller, simpler, unsmoggy country, to study it as thoroughly in six months as I have done in as many decades.

Alexis de Tocqueville, you are drafted for the job of showing us whether or not the conglomerates that have arisen among us are an essential part of our national bent. That's an honor, sir, since many other experts would gladly take the job. You are picked because you were here before conglomerates or any of their forerunners existed. The Industrial Revolution had only barely taken off in Great Britain and Europe, and you landed on our shores before it made an impact here.

Further, you had that prime virtue of an investigative reporter: honesty. You were at once so enthusiastic about our democracy, our love for equality, that you wrote your book to hold it up as a model to the people of your troubled country. Still, you were brutally frank in your description of our ugly and archaic slave economy, which you recognized as destructive to black slaves, white slaveholders, and the struggling "free" of each color alike. You were frankly critical, too, of the harsh treatment we visited on the gentle native peoples of our land, treatment you feared would lead to their extinction.

Tell us, De Tocqueville, what is our national character? Tell what seems to you our most prominent characteristic.

"*Bonjour, madame.* I have been invoked many times, but you are the first to bring my spirit back to earth. I have already answered your question. Surely you did not forget. It is on page 513 of your Anchor Books edition of my work:

> Americans of all ages, all stations in life, and all types of disposition are forever forming associations . . . not only commercial and industrial . . . religious, moral, serious, futile, very general and very limited, immensely large and very minute. Americans combine to give fêtes, found seminaries, build churches, distribute books and send missionaries to the antipodes. Hospitals, prisons and schools take shape in this way. Finally, if they want to proclaim a truth or propagate some feeling by the encouragement of a great example, they form an association.

I tried to explain to my ghostly friend that conglomerates, those associations *par excellence*, were great aggregates of people rolled into balls; "associations large" indeed, "commercial and industrial," to use his words, designed to make inflated profits for associations of stockholders—but he could not understand what I was talking about. He insisted that such things would not be tolerated in the democratic, egalitarian, and peaceful society he had once held up as a model.

There was nothing for it but to make a flight of the imagination together over the land, after a demonstration of my needle's-eye method and an attempt to prepare him for the congestion and smog that makes the method necessary.

That attempt was a failure. He must have been suffering from a monstrous 150-year jet lag. His cool Gallic objectivity seemed hopelessly scrambled. He kept babbling questions about where the farmhouses and farmyards were, while we flew over miles of high-producing agrifactories. And he wanted to know why most of the streets looked so empty and so foul, as we flew over the great suburbs to the dirtier cities.

He pointed to the bumper-to-bumper commuters, and was terrified by what he saw as metallic dragons. Then, when a crash piled up some of the cars, and the drivers poured out into the road, he was sickened by what he thought were monster intestines gushing from great wounded serpents.

Hopeless, I thought, and I let the vision fade, glaring at his book in disgust. Then I remembered a remark of a friend from overseas: "If you want to really understand your country, Jo, and get to its very heart, go to Disneyland."

"Alexis," I cried hypocritically, "we need a vacation. We are going to Disneyland!"

When we walked through the gate, the years fell off our shoulders, mine with a big enough thump and his with a great ghostly whimper.

"Now I'm glad I came back to your country," said my friend, and I was, too. "This is more like the America I remember, so clean and homey, the nice little country towns, all the golden dreams and fantasies. Peace and fun and happy faces."

He did not even mind the long slow lines and the crowds. "They are like the fairs and carnivals that used to be in both our countries, but being America, they are much bigger and more exciting, of course."

We kept pouring out money for food and rides and souvenirs, but he did not mind that either. It was my money. And it did not bother me much because somewhere here in the heart of Disneyland we were going to find the answer to the key question: Are the conglomerates part of our national character, bone of our American bone?

We took all the rides and saw it all: the Indian Village and the African Safari, and Fantasyland. But in Disneyland we are all children again (some of the crowd are even children still), and what do children care about conglomerates?

It was a wonderful holiday, and Alexis had recovered from his jet lag when we returned to my little apartment to puzzle out the secret hidden in the heart of our outing.

"That is the real America, Josephine," said Alexis. "You see, you don't see all that pollution there *—all the filth and violence in the streets and the anger and loneliness on the peoples' faces. There were none of those great metallic monsters traveling along at a snail's pace, and none of those ugly billboards. Small is still beautiful there. How your Disney must have loved children!"

"But, Alexis," I said gently, "Disney Enterprises, Incorporated, is a conglomerate. Walt Disney has been dead a long time, and he died childless. In fact, it is said that he did not like children. But he did not die without heirs. Disney Enterprises, the world's biggest entertainment conglomerate, has amusement parks scattered all over the country, and many, many imitators. And that's not all: remember Mickey and Minnie Mouse, Donald Duck—the whole community of Disney characters? There are comic books and storybooks and television series, Disney toys, Disney clothes, Disney appliances, and Disney furniture distributed all over the world. And we hardly ever have a G-rated movie anymore—which means it is suitable for children without parental guidance—that isn't a Disney product.

"You noticed all those cash registers playing their lively tunes to our quarters and dollars. Every year money flows into Disney Enterprises from just about every country in the world. In the year ending September 30, 1979, the profits after taxes were $113.8 million; gross revenues, $796.8 million."[1]

We both sipped our wine thoughtfully. Then Alexis smiled and hit the table with his fist.

"I have it," he said. "This Disney Enterprises is the greatest of all the conglomerates, so rich and powerful that it dares to defy all the others, to be a traitor to its system, to make its own rules."

I thanked him and neatly tucked him back into his book. I might need him again to help with another question, but on

* I did not have the heart to tell him that the usually smoggy air was clean for a change because it had rained recently.

this one he had given all the help he could. His page 513 and his good company in Disneyland had cleared away the cobwebs, and now the view through the needle's eye was beginning to take shape.

De Tocqueville had not been right in every detail, but much of what he saw, as was always true for him, was clear and honest.

Disney Enterprises is not the greatest conglomerate. It does not even appear on the *Fortune* 500. Still, it is one of the greatest entertainment conglomerates, and for the following reasons.

Walt Disney sensed in his bones all the things his fellow countrymen, women, and children were troubled by in the real-world, twentieth-century U.S.A., so he created a dream world for us. He turned himself into the American Dream, and thanks to him even the poor, the lonely, and the depressed can journey to the most real never-never land the world has ever seen, walking through its gate back into childhood and into childhood's faith that dreams come true.

Right inside the gate not only our own adulthood falls away, but our country's maturity does too, and we are back in those days before the common carriers (the railroads and their successors) and the uncommon oil kings began to roll all our magic carpets up into balls.

All our people—young and old, rich and poor, women and men, educated and ignorant—are welcomed into Disneyland. The smiling, shining, friendly faces of the employees show an eagerness to serve us, to keep our miniature America squeaky clean for us, to feed us, to entertain us, and to send us back to the other America outside the gate with treasured memories and sturdy souvenirs.

Again, De Tocqueville was partly right. Disney Enterprises is in some measure a traitor to its fellow conglomerates. In this case, the creed—to us the profits, to them the cost—is only partially lived up to.

True, we pour our dollars into the chiming cash registers, but the charges are pretty honest and fair, and we not only pay for what we get, we get what we pay for.

Disney Enterprises does not load down taxpayers with hidden costs for cleaning its streets and buildings, maintaining its roads, policing its grounds, and providing services for young and old. It provides equal-opportunity jobs* and costumes and grooming to thousands of people, and though nobody has ever accused it of overpaying its employees (since the days when Walt Disney locked out his cartoonists and animators because they asked for a minimum wage), it has paid as much as the law and its employees require it to.

De Tocqueville's ghost was right. Conglomerates are indeed alien to our national character, described so well by the living Alexis on page 513. And Disney Enterprises, Inc., is the exception that proves the rule.

Love and concern for ourselves and our fellows are the magnets that draw Americans into so many associations "immensely large and very minute," but those human emotions are not the magnets that roll the immensely large conglomerates into immensely larger balls.

Why do people, after they have amassed more money than they or their descendants can spend in a hundred years, form corporate associations to double or triple the load? One man gave a clue: "I said I would retire at seventy," said a corporate executive, "but what could I do that's as much fun as this game?"[2] "Game" is the clue word, and the name of the game is power.

The full name of the *Fortune* 500 is *Fortune 500 Largest U.S. Industrial Corporations.* Every May, *Fortune* magazine publishes its justly celebrated issue bearing this title. The *Fortune* 500 is to the conglomerate game what the Kentucky Derby is to horseracing and the World Series Pennant is to baseball.

In the May 1978 issue, the 500 winners had totaled $1.2 trillion in sales. No use bothering to write out that figure. The number of zeros in a billion is tiresome enough. Millions of dollars mean spendable wealth; billions, earth-shaking power. But a trillion?

* After a bit of a fuss.

In the conglomerate game, the contenders who do not succeed in making enough mergers, acquisitions, and diversification to make the 500 are still in the running for consolation prizes. The *Fortune* Second 500 is published later. And then there is the nonindustrial *Fortune* 50.

The rules of the game demand that each conglomerate have one supreme power, and if that power is threatened, then— well, the financial news is full of accounts of jousts between rival contenders and the unseating of the weakest ones.

Teamwork, equality, and democracy do not underlie the rules of the game. *Hierarchy* is a word common in the accounts. Increasingly, reports tell of mergers not democratically agreed to by two conglomerates, but pursued relentlessly by one, until the pursuer either is driven off or forces the quarry to its knees.

My buoyant mood, generated by our Disneyland holiday and by De Tocqueville's happy recognition of our true native bent, began to wilt as I thought about the actions of those thousand or so game players, whose bargaining chips are the lives of the 220 million U.S. citizens. I needed reassurance. I reached for my folder labeled "Self-Help." I was looking for some recent evidence as to our true native bent. I *knew* conglomeratism did not represent the American character, but how to prove it?

I began to pull out random items: First, Herkimer. To the conglomerate that owned it, Herkimer was a library-furniture factory in a small town in upstate New York. The plant did not have enough profit potential to warrant efforts on the parent corporation's part to bring its old factories up to standard. The conglomerate's alternative, the obvious choice, was to take its loss as a tax writeoff and close the plant down.

To the 270 people on Herkimer's administrative and factory payroll, the conglomerate's divestiture of the factory meant unemployment or the uprooting of 270 families. To the town where Herkimer was located, it meant loss of a major payroll and heavier tax burdens for the whole community.

It's not easy for employees—no, ex-employees—white-collar and blue, to form a cooperative and buy out a factory of limited growth potential. Happily, this particular group found a colleague in a perceptive public servant, New York Lieutenant Governor Mary Ann Krupsak. Today, Herkimer is a cooperative making a profit for its 270 employee-owners, and whose annual payroll is $3.5 million.[3]

Next, in shuffling through my "Self-Help" file, I found a short note about the Mighty Mite Lumber Cooperative in Humboldt County, California. Again, an enterprise had been created, when its previous conglomerate owners decided to move to lower-wage, higher-profit country. Now its 75 owner-operators are keeping their homes, their jobs, and their lives together.

The leaders of a worldwide organization called Quality of Work Life predict that "worker-community ownership of U.S. firms will expand slightly as profit-minded corporations sell off aging, unprofitable plants that provide jobs to thousands of workers in the nation's industrial belt."[4]

The Keyston Company of San Francisco had foreshadowed the worker-owner trend. Noel L. Arthur, grandson of the founder of Keyston Saddle Company, is now chairman of the board, and Keyston is owned by its 150 employees; does a $15-million-a-year volume in products ranging from saddles to seats for buses, airplanes, and restaurants.[5]

Brooks, probably San Francisco's busiest photographic supply store, has a $1.1-million employee stock ownership plan and has recently opened several branch stores. Going into Brooks used to be like trying to shop in a commuter terminal during peak hours, but now it's fun. The profit-sharing employees have the incentive and the time to participate with customers in problem solving.

In keeping with the employees-as-owners trend is the growing popularity of the employee stock ownership plan (ESOP).[6] This idea was developed ten years or so ago by a man named Louis Kelso, and was at first received skeptically. The theory was that every employee of a business should be made into a capitalist, with an investment in the business and a stake in the profits. ESOP has been and still is opposed by many labor leaders, employees, and banks. Against the powerful squeeze of rising agribusiness, many small agricultural cooperatives, regardless of their efforts at banding together, were crushed.*

Milt Moskovitz told the story of an agricultural cooperative that survived against heavy odds, and flourishes.[7]

> Ocean Spray Cranberries, Inc., a cooperative that bands together 705 cranberry growers in five states, formerly had their sales closely tied to the maintenance of a tradition: the bird that graced the table at Thanksgiving. . . .
>
> One of the early cancer scares, implicating a herbicide used by some growers, knocked the cranberry farmers for a loop in 1959. Their sales went into an eclipse.
>
> Emerging from that depression in 1963, the Ocean Spray cooperative turned into an aggressive marketing organization that spawned a whole new line of products . . . all bearing the Ocean Spray brand and backed by big bucks put into television advertising . . . recruited top flight marketing professionals from the corporate world . . . [made] $160 million in sales for the year . . . and is now branching out, merging with citrus and prune cooperatives.

I realized De Tocqueville had been right. What could express our native character better than the formation of cooperatives? The American spirit was forged by cooperative effort and worker ownership long before conglomeratism—or Marxism, for that matter—was heard of. Not only does this mean that the citizens of our country have been serving as unwilling pawns in a game alien to their sense of fair play, it means that to fight—if fight we can—against the conglomerate trend would be an honest battle.

---

* Among these was "The Egg Basket of the World," Petaluma, California, with its hundreds of cooperatized poultry farms throughout the 1950s, which was crushed when agripoultry rose in low-wage southern states.

11

〜〜〜〜〜〜〜〜〜〜〜〜〜〜〜〜〜〜〜〜〜〜〜

THE DREAM AND THE COMPUTER

Martin Luther King, Jr., had a dream, and this chapter is my dream: of an America safe and clean and healthy; rich and warmly human, for my grandchildren, and for all our children.

To begin with we want our government to get back in democratic control, and therefore to seize control of inflation and taxation and recession.

We want to work. Everybody wants to work. Forget the twaddle about hardcore unemployables. Everybody is potentially employable when given the opportunity to do work that makes sense, yields a decent living, does not hurt others, and is based on today's realities: automation and higher production in shorter work weeks.

We don't want to destroy the industrial giants who built the conglomerate system; we don't want to destroy what good qualities exist within that system. We want to get the conglomerates under control—democratic control.

In my dream, we put our new computer technology to work to help us achieve these goals fairly and nonviolently.

Most of us think of computers as inhuman, impersonal machines that, once they misrepresent some facet of our lives, hang on like terriers to their blooper, and shake us the way a terrier shakes a rat.

Many of us blame computers for the constant encroachment

on our lives of Murphy's Law: "If anything can go wrong, it will." In fact, computers, along with overpopulation, bear the responsibility in most of our laments for the inhumanity of the society in which we live.

In the early days of computer technology, these machines were massive, costly, complicated, and completely under the control of the most powerful conglomerates and conglomerate-dominated branches of the government. There they exercised their enormous capacity to nose into every cranny of our lives.

Today, the huge, costly, nosey computers still exist, but simplified memory banks have also become available to moderate-income people to be used for game playing and home-appliance control. More significant, a large and increasingly varied population of computer programmers and operators has been engaged at all levels of industry and services to process the flow of work-related information.

Come, dream with me and my imaginary electronic machine.

Imagine that into a computer's memory bank we have fed all the figures compiled regarding our nation's wealth and optimum living standards. We've asked, and the machine has told us, just how much money the family of a chief executive officer in a conglomerate would have to spend to maintain a reasonable share of the good things in our society: security, homes (one or two, spacious but not palatial—that's gone out of style), several cars, travel, and recreational equipment and facilities such as boats, horses, and a ski lodge.

Our country is so rich that the figure could be set pretty high. Let's say (not entirely with tongue in cheek) that the computer shows it would take $1 million a year for our chief executive officer to start to maintain such ownings with the incentive of doubling the ceiling after the computer dream has taken shape. Next, let's ask the computer how much money would constitute the capital investment needed to produce such a return. Suppose the answer is $20 million mid-1979 dollars.

We could then call on the computer for more complex projections. Now that we've practiced on working out the income necessary to maintain an individual and his family in the style to which they are accustomed, let's go right to the heart of the matter to ask how the great conglomerates might be divested of their diversified components in excess of the permissible ceiling, that is, of the surplus only useful for power.

The answer is not so very complex: the conglomerates have shown us the way. They divest themselves whenever it suits them. The divestitures of the small library-furniture company in Herkimer, and the Humboldt County lumber operations described in the preceding chapter are two of many hundreds of examples.

There's really no need to work out a plan to save the divested components. Herkimer, Mighty Mite, Hallmark, Keyston Company, Brooks, Ocean Spray, and many, many more enterprises are living, functioning exhibits of our national bent for cooperative work, which makes every worker a capitalist with a stake in the organization.

Nor do we need to prove to ourselves that nationalization (that is, state ownership of the means of production, the idea at the heart of Marxist socialism or communism) is alien to our American character. We equate government ownership with bureaucracy, and most agree that more bureaucracy is not what we need.

We know that when theoretical knowledge and practical experience are applied equally in a cooperative venture, the result is the antithesis of bureaucracy. In short, we don't need the computer to tell us what we believe about ourselves. Its great value is in storing and keeping available all the information bearing on a problem.

Imagine, then, that the conglomerates have been peacefully divested of their excess power. The machine is next instructed to list the options each citizen would have under these new circumstances: 1. Perhaps the opportunity of a career within one of the conglomerate nuclei, which would still be rich, well organized, and able to maintain a sound profit potential; or 2. an employee-ownership share in one of the divested components, possibly in the same company in which the person had been employed; or 3. self-employment in the surviving and soon flourishing free-enterprise system, consisting of small and middle-sized businesses, factories, and farms, all surging with new vitality on their release from the conglomerate squeeze and encouraged by the government, which has already expressed its appreciation for the contribution of free enterprise to the whole economy.

The initial response to the wild dream of peacefully divesting the conglomerates of their power would probably be a protest at the naiveté of the proposal. Everyone knows that any new laws to that effect would be shadow-boxed into meaninglessness by the conglomerates and their advocates within the government.

But the beauty of the dream is that we could begin *without the passage of new laws.* We as citizens could insist on the firm enforcement of the laws we have.

In fact, giant steps have already been taken toward realizing the dream. The public has grown increasingly aware of the crimes, sins, and misdemeanors committed by most conglomerates. Handicapped though we are by the might of the *Fortune* 500 public-interest advocates, people have, in recent years, been at work on many fronts: exposing, opposing, bringing to judgment, demanding, and winning convictions in the courts, and exacting large fines for irresponsible and destructive action.* Not so very many years ago, suits were seldom brought against corporations for such offenses. When brought, they were seldom won; and those few that were won, after long, costly court maneuvering, were usually dismissed with polite slaps on the corporate wrists.

At present, a whole new generation of tough, concerned whistle-blowers—mostly attorneys and their backups of concerned, disillusioned people, as well as some people in government—have the conglomerates running a little scared.

However, they aren't scared enough, because the diversified giants wield great power in the Supreme Court, appointed by

---

* Examples: Ford Pinto, Silkwood verdict, Goodyear tires, and so forth.

the administrations under their control. Still, the power is never as complete as they would wish, for the great prestige and dignity of this ultimate tribunal on law and constitutionality sometimes have an ennobling effect on the body of rich and aging men who uphold the existing system.

An increasingly concerned and well-informed public, which has recently been demonstrating a growing confidence in its own judgment, the same confidence that inspired the proud words of the Declaration of Independence, would not have to impeach or pack the Supreme Court to bring it to honorable support for the rule of law, divorced from the rule of power. The computer would probably project that a widespread popular demand for the imposition of heavy penalties against conglomerates for the criminal disregard for human life and welfare—such as were demonstrated by the Karen Silkwood case; the near disaster at Three Mile Island; the Chicago DC-10 tragedy—would turn the tide toward impartial enforcement of already existing laws.

The prognosis for a redress of these grievances is not unfavorable. Imagine the computer fingering for prosecution every irresponsible act that ever damaged or jeopardized public health, safety, or well-being, and computing the full cost of reparations (those which can be translated into mere monetary terms) to be paid by guilty conglomerates. We could expect a lengthy printout itemizing the now unimaginable costs of oil spills, blowouts, explosions, and other avoidable losses of our precious world resources. And think of the estimates regarding radioactive-waste disposal and the poisoning of soil, water, and air by profit-making chemicals and industrial waste.

Let us imagine that all available data about each of the *Fortune* 500 will be fed into the memory bank of our computer. Then will follow the relentless investigation of each clue pointing to a disregard of laws, each violation of rights to life and safety, each instance of damage to the environment and to our own purses; each potential encroachment on the tax laws; each rumor of collusion with organized crime, of bribery, or of other forms of influence peddling within any branch of the government; and each claim of false or misleading advertising.

Imagine an initial prosecution of, say, 25 percent of the most flagrant cases of abuse followed by a computerized study of all the products of those targeted conglomerates. From the latter would be selected a small list of those products most profitable to the conglomerates and least beneficial to the consumers. Then imagine half of us simply cutting these products off our shopping lists.

Next, let's have the computer study the labor relations of the targeted conglomerates, printing out information on collusion with high union officials and on violations of health-and-safety codes and other laws relating to the well-being and fair treatment of workers. Suppose that a confused portion of the staff of the conglomerates under investigation were to remain loyal to their employers. This would still leave a substantial percentage, intelligent and informed, to make reasonable and legal demands for redress.

The sum effect of such a campaign, resting on the computer's most fundamental capacity to make projections, would be to use the conglomerates' own methods of crushing or bringing into conformity any opposition to their power. But here the attacks would be mounted not for private profit but for the public welfare. And they would be legal.

There are other things we could do to right our system. For example, corporations could be forced to pay for the experience and contacts gained by their employees who were trained on our tax dollars as employees of the federal and state governments. And perhaps corporations should have to pay us back our tax dollars in the form of a one-time payment equivalent to five years of the salary the employee would be earning.

In the scenario I have dreamed up, all the chief executive officers of the targeted conglomerates, and probably those not directly targeted too, because they are intelligent people, would undoubtedly get the message.

After careful thought, they would probably decide to cut

their losses. Regretfully, to be sure. The game had been good clean fun, from their point of view. Now all that energy, intelligence, and drive would have to find some other outlet. They would accept the cutback of their financial activities to one segment of each of their conglomerate empires, and for an income too low to continue to play the power game.

Some CEOs would opt to divert their energies into doing the best possible job for the new society. Many precedents exist for this sort of shift in perspective: industrial achievers who found industry limited in scope and interest and went on to create hospital and health plans, magnificent art and book collections; millionaires who worked for international friendship, for the advancement of science, and for the continued development of every branch of the arts.

Other CEOs would undoubtedly be less adaptable. These would probably publicly acquiesce while secretly plotting a counterstrategy. Perhaps they would simply await the collapse of the whole economy, expecting the cooperatives and free-enterprise projects to fail in good time, thus allowing the restoration of the conglomerates. Possibly they would envision such a restoration as occurring without any pretense of democracy.

The computer would be too smart for these plotters, once its accuracy in identifying lawbreakers and in estimating damages had won over the American people. At present, the greatest stumbling block to broad support of such a cleanup effort is our modesty, the self-doubt we characteristically suffer regarding our own intelligence and concerns. This same self-doubt is fed by the artificial division that exists between theoreticians and practical people.

With that stumbling block removed and our practical self-confidence restored, no FBI, CIA, or any other undercover, spying agency would be needed to throw the glare of public awareness upon efforts made by the fragmented conglomerate system to regain its former power. Such efforts, made and exposed, would be met with the full force of the law. After serving maximum legal prison sentences, plotters on behalf of conglomerates, impoverished by maximum legal fines, would have to start life over near the bottom of the economic ladder.

Now for the role of the war industries in our computer's scenario. In this projection, the CEOs of the *Fortune* 500 and the *Fortune* Second 500 have yielded to the combined might of democracy, equality, and the law. Each has agreed to select one component of his or her conglomerate empire and divest the rest for conversion to employee stock ownership plans.

Now, each of the thousand giants has probably at least one extremely remunerative war-related industry tucked unobtrusively into its portfolio. Should each CEO select this particular unit as the one to keep, then each emperor would stand in an awesome public glare, with his profit motive hanging out.

Rather than risk such public exposure, the conglomerates might be persuaded to relinquish their war-industry components. All the country's massive war industries would then be divested, and offered for conversion to owner-operated cooperatives. (True, this might need some firm persuading.)

One safeguard of national security might be the addition of war industries to our list of nonprofit organizations: schools, churches, cultural and scientific institutions, and, for the short time they would still be needed, welfare organizations.

At this point in the computer dream, the machine might get somewhat hysterical and pour forth a waist-high stack of wide-sheeted, accordion-folded printouts. The projections on these sheets would have to do with the competence of scientific breakthroughs in solving our most distressing health and environmental problems and the speed with which the solutions could be accomplished. These cures would be made possible by the release of a vast wealth of scientists, technicians, and potential scientists and technicians now serving or destined for dreary bondage to the war machine. We would set them free to work on projects relating to abundant, joyous living; to an ever widening knowledge of our planet, its potential dangers and potential enrichment.

For scientific freedom to be realized—and for every other

kind of freedom to be realized—the computer must dream up an answer to our number-one problem: inflation, passed over up to this point, but never forgotten.

The truth is, there is no need here for new dreams. One need only think back over thirty-five years of ever-more-frequent mergers—in fact, of hysterical merger mania—and literally thousands of bottom lines greater than the profits of the half-dozen richest men of forty years ago, to see that conglomerates have learned how to benefit. All that is needed, then, is to computerize all that conglomerates know about taking advantage of inflation, which is really knowledge of how to control the measures that would stabilize the currency and prevent inflation in reverse.

Once these currency-stabilizing measures were extracted and proposed, there would be little danger of opposition from the chief executive officers of the divested conglomerate core units. Their merger game ended, they would have as much to lose as the rest of us from inflation, and as much to gain as we all do from dollar stabilization.

But with all the printout sheets pouring from the computer—and having unmerged the conglomerates, restored our country to an economy with a stable currency, and initially slashed our income taxes and other oppressive parts of our tax burden—we would still have a mass of problems to deal with.

First, that unemployment rate. Now, even in the best of times unemployment among young people of ethnic and other minorities stands at approximately the rate for the whole population during the nadir of the Depression.* Piddling attacks have been mounted by such programs as Johnson's Great Society (triggered by the Watts riots) and sundry bureaucratic training programs, but they all shy away from the heart of the problem: dwindling employment from the export of capital and plants; maintenance of the standard work week despite almost

---

* No figures were kept during the Depression, but the most frequently cited estimate is 25 percent unemployment.

forty years of increasing work stress; and the continued diminishing of free enterprise.

"Yankee, come home" might be a new computerized slogan, signaling the offer of shortened work weeks and shared benefits for cooperatively studied and solved unit-productivity problems.

Next, with a wicked, electronic chortle, the computer might print out a shocking proposal representing a total about-face of the antagonists in our current most heated controversy: reinstatement of peacetime draft registration.

Different exponents offer different versions of draft registration. In one plan, all draft-age men are to be registered; in another both men and women. One plan ends with registration, its purpose to keep information at hand in case of need. Another is for registration plus an option of a term of military or civilian service of a good-doing sort.

Now, imagine this jingoist, bureaucratic, peacetime-draft-registration proposal being seized upon by the dreaming computer and redesigned into an entirely different kind of project. There would be a national registration, but it would not be administered by bureaucratic agencies. Rather, registration would be accomplished by communities. It would be leisurely, cooperative, and community centered, and it would provide each segment of the country—rich and poor, North and South, high- and low-employment areas—with its own census. First, it would reveal all the unmet needs in the community: for housing, sanitation, food, child care, services for the old and the physically dependent, education, clean and rich environments, crime and corrections, recreation, transportation.

Then, and only then, with their lists of priorities full and clear, the communities would each take a census of available human resources: men and women; young and old; unemployed, employed, underemployed, wastefully misemployed.

One of the first steps taken by each community would be to meet its own needs regarding its computer or computers and a well-trained corps of programmers. Imagine the incentives here for self-motivated training and education, and the acquisition of work discipline. Imagine, too, the rapid effect of such projects on the mental and physical health of every community.

Another benefit would duplicate what is generally agreed to be the one good result of a war: the breaking down of social barriers; that is, the assertion of each person's place in the human family that occurs when a people are united in the determination to triumph over a common threat. No need to doubt, then, that cooperative, community-oriented undertakings would lead to a steady bettering of lives.

Imagine the 65 percent of the American people who have disenfranchised themselves by no longer bothering to vote returning to the polls with renewed hope—coming to the appreciation that only through our combined intelligence and strength can we take back our democratic system and end the days when elections are for candidates acceptable only to the conglomerates.

In my dream I have made the computer serve us all. Perhaps more experienced minds than mine can devise the specific programs that would bring our lives back into balance. But I am sure of one thing: any solution will be based on a public exposure of the truth. In my imaginings, the computer has served as the conduit for the truth because it is able to express facts without judging them. My certainty in the possibility of a solution lies in my knowledge that the facts lie on the side of truth—leading to liberty and justice for all.

Better minds than mine must work out the means of breaking up the conglomerates. Better minds there are—brilliant, learned, professional minds and sensible, experienced, practical minds. By using them together we can release free enterprise from the conglomerate squeeze and provide ourselves with work places for the production of safe, high quality goods and services. In doing so we will regain our old, well-loved American know-how and rid ourselves of the stresses of inflation, inflated taxes, and fear of national disintegration.

12 〰〰〰〰〰〰〰〰〰〰〰〰〰〰〰〰〰〰〰〰〰〰〰

ON A NOTE OF CHEER

On Lincoln's Birthday, 1978, a town in mountainous Lassen County, California, with the forgettable name of Westwood, California, turned off its lights.

On that day, probably only a few hundred friends, relations, employers, and creditors of Westwood's twenty-eight hundred residents knew that the town existed, and was in Lassen County, in the Sierra Nevadas. By Washington's birthday, 1978, Westwood had friends from England to Australia and enthusiastic admirers all over our country. Reporters and photographers had scrambled over the snowy, icy mountain roads, searched out the village of some eight hundred modest frame houses tucked away in a fold of the mountains, and told its story.

During the past year, electricity rates had doubled and tripled for the rate payers of Westwood. There had been no problem about gas rates, because it was unprofitable for the gas company to pipe gas to this thinly populated region. The town's heating and cooking were done by electricity where connections were affordable or unavoidable. Otherwise, wood or oil were used.

In the best of times, and even when the greatest economy is practiced, electricity is an important item of the budget for communities like Westwood. Those of us who live in cities do not realize until we move to small towns that utility rates are not based on the egalitarian principle of one-meter/one-rate, but rather on the profits of the stockholders. Thus, rates are lowest in cities, and there they are lowest for the heaviest users; rates are higher in middle-sized towns, and considerably, often painfully, higher still in rural areas.

The winter of 1977–1978 had not been the best of times. The normally high rate of the winter before had doubled or, in a number of billings, tripled and worse.

The Westwood population consists mostly of lumber and construction workers, trees being the main product of the area. Another portion of the population consists of retired people, who often head for the hills in search of peaceful scenery and a balanced budget. A third identifiable group is composed of "longhaired Lassen College students, who have earned the town the nickname of 'Wastewood' in the area."[1] Small-businesspeople, surviving comparatively well, since the area does not have enough profit potential to attract conglomerates, make up the balance of the residents.

Too varied a population, one would think, to manage to unite in common purpose, even given De Tocqueville's observation of our national habit of "forming associations to . . . proclaim a truth or propagate some feeling by the encouragement of a great example." In 1978 the incentive must have been strong indeed to cut across the diverse viewpoints of retired people, longhaired students, construction workers, and businesspeople. It was.

The rate payers at first had treated the sums on their 1977–1978 bills as errors, but they had exhausted the usual appeals meant to correct billing mistakes. Not only had the utility company's officials (San Francisco–based California Pacific Utilities Company) developed a hearing problem when questioned about those bills, but the public officials who are paid to investigate public problems had wax in their ears as well.

Westwood's residents had received silly nonanswers in response to their complaints and questions: for example, that Pacific Gas and Electric had raised its charges to CPU following the previous year's droughts; that the well-being of the utility companies had to come first, since without it there would be no power; that their wattage, meter readings, and billings could not possibly be in error.

Finding all their routes of appeal exhausted, three Westwood women, Pauline Asmus, Paulette Benner, and Patty McCormac, chatting over coffee, hit on a last-ditch plan. They drafted a letter to the local mimeographed weekly paper, *The Pinecone Press*, urging their neighbors to turn off their power.

"You know how a small town is," said McCormac. "Everybody knew about the blackout four days before the letter came out."

The point had been to attract enough attention throughout the area to shake the officials into an investigation of the rate hikes. But would enough people be willing to stand the dark, the cold, the sacrifice of television—the community's only source of entertainment, and the lack of all the other conveniences we Americans find indispensable—in the doubtful hope of making their point? Working against the plan was also the realization that the eight hundred houses of the town were for the most part drafty and poorly insulated. It was no plan for summer soldiers.

But it worked. Of course it did. And—as the story went out all over the state, then the nation, and then the world; as interest and sympathy came in from such diverse groups as the Jarvis-McCann tax-reform committee and Ralph Nader's Raiders; as sympathizers far and wide pulled their power switches—utility officials and public agencies finally heard the message.

They investigated. The primary problem had been the unlawful overloading of circuits, a sloppy and hazardous solution to earlier problems of insufficient wattage. Computer billing errors and careless meter readings were also found.

On Washington's Birthday, Westwood turned the power back on. The community had enjoyed ten days of potluck dinners and candlelit sociability in their homes heated by wood fires.

"It was better than TV," said a teenage spokesperson.

"We have egg on our face," said an official of the utility.

The people of Westwood had followed a time-honored American tradition.

In 1773 some young people in Boston boarded a British ship and threw chests of tea into the harbor.

In the 1820s, some escaped slaves and northern sympathizers established the Underground Railway.

On December 1, 1955, Rosa Parks sat down in the "white" section of a Montgomery, Alabama, bus and would not budge.

Each of those actions made clear and simple statements about problems that needed solving. Statements without words.

After public attention was focused on the evils of living in colonialism under a feudal aristocracy and monarch, Tom Paine wrote *Common Sense*. He had found the words to unite the people against the problem.

After public attention was captured by the simple courage of the Underground Railway, Harriet Beecher Stowe put the evil of slavery into a moving and exciting story, *Uncle Tom's Cabin*.

After Rosa Parks sat where she belonged, and not where she was told to sit, Martin Luther King, Jr., put into stirring words the need to end segregation.

The people of Westwood performed a simple, week-long act in February 1978, and I wish I had the brevity of Paine, the imagination of Stowe, and the eloquence of King, to put into words the statement their action made. It said that when big, powerful conglomerated enterprises put their profits and the welfare of their stockholders ahead of the welfare and safety of their customers; when they brush aside honesty and respect for law in their unenlightened self-interest, and push the public servants who should control them into upholding them; then it is time to unite and find simple, direct, legal and nonviolent means to finish up the job begun by the Boston Tea Party, the Underground Railway, Rosa Parks, and the people of Westwood.

We still have taxation without representation and the tyranny of a gang of feudal robber barons; we still have millions of people enslaved by joblessness and hopelessness; and we still have many kinds of segregation all around us.

And will have as long as we let a few thousand chief executive officers sneak control of our White House, Congress, and Supreme Court.

If we listen to what the people of Westwood told us without words: that action must be simple; clearly targeted to cut across lines of age and interest; never confused by a lot of pretentious words: then ways can be found to unroll this colossal ball the conglomerates are rolling us all up in: inflation, unemployment, debts, and war. We have the Constitution on our side. We've just let them bluff us out of using it.

NOTES

NOTES TO CHAPTER 1

1. Milt Moskovitz, "Money Tree: Products Make Strange Bedfellows," *San Francisco Chronicle*, November 19, 1977, p. 13.
2. *Handbook of Labor Statistics 1978, Bulletin 2000 of the U.S. Department of Labor: Bureau of Labor Statistics:* "Table 150: Union Membership as Proportion of Labor Force."
3. " 'Dangers Posed by Trend' FTC Chief Assails Mergers," *San Francisco Chronicle*, May 8, 1979, p. 24.

NOTES TO CHAPTER 2

1. "What Americans Spent on Vehicles," *San Francisco Chronicle*, July 7, 1978, p. 19.

   American motorists spent $376 billion—more than $1800 per man, woman, and child in the United States—to own and operate their cars and trucks during 1977 . . . [report of] Hertz Corp., in an annual estimate of automotive operating costs . . . total U.S. motor vehicle outlays have more than doubled in the past five years . . . passenger car expenses amounted to $1904 per car . . . 27.1% of the average American's personal income.

2. "Motor Vehicles Multiplying Faster Than U.S. People," *San Francisco Chronicle*, August 29, 1979, p. 6.

   Anthony Downs, a senior fellow at the Brookings Institution, reported that at the end of 1977, there were about 129 million vehicles in the United States for 217 million people.

And he said, "Our vehicle population is growing 2.5 times as fast in absolute numbers" as the human population.

In an article in the AFL-CIO *Federationist* magazine, reprinted from *Traffic Quarterly*, Downs wrote: "The United States is experiencing an amazing, yet almost unnoticed, 'population explosion'—not of people but of automotive vehicles."

3. "Deaths Going Up, Along with Speed," *San Francisco Examiner*, May 14, 1978, p. 7.

Highway fatalities, no longer reflecting the 55 mph speed limit slow-down, rose nearly 4% in 1977 . . . in all forms of transportation totaled 52,154 . . . 46,880 in highway accidents.

NOTES TO CHAPTER 3

1. "Shipping Industries Caught by Glut in Global Capacity," *San Francisco Chronicle*, May 8, 1978, p. 27.
2. Robert C. Keith, *Ocean World*, "The Making of the Worst Oil Spill," *San Francisco Sunday Examiner & Chronicle, Sunday Punch*, July 2, 1978, p. 2.
3. Ibid.
4. "The French Oil Spill Leaves a Residue of Bitterness," *San Francisco Chronicle*, May 3, 1978, p. B-4.
5. Jimmy Breslin, "An Oil Spill So Bad They'd Like Another," *San Francisco Sunday Examiner & Chronicle, Sunday Punch*, August 3, 1978, p. 2.
6. "Landowner Tried to Halt Drilling at Blowout Site," *San Francisco Chronicle*, May 14, 1978, p. 8.
7. "Fiery Geyser of Oil," *San Francisco Chronicle*, September 22, 1978, p. 5.
8. "Oil Stockpile Still Burning in Louisiana," *San Francisco Chronicle*, July 25, 1976, p. 13.
9. "OPEC's Impact: How 1973 Shaped the Oil World," *San Francisco Chronicle*, October 23, 1978, p. 56.

The big oil internationals—Exxon, Mobil, Texaco, Gulf, Standard Oil of California, British Petroleum, and Royal Dutch Shell—the so-called "Seven Sisters" . . . for half a century had dominated most aspects of the global oil business from drilling to shipping to refining to marketing.

10. "Hearings into Explosions of Rail Tankers," *San Francisco Chronicle*, March 21, 1978, p. 15.
11. "House Told of LNG Perils at Hearing," *San Francisco Chronicle*, February 21, 1978, p. 8.

12. "World's Oil Tankers Becoming Obsolete," *San Francisco Chronicle*, December 22, 1978, p. 31.
13. Marcie Rasmussen, "The Oil Glut Behind the Rise in Gas Prices," *San Francisco Chronicle*, June 21, 1978, p. 8.
14. "Shipping Industry Caught by Glut in Global Capacity," *San Francisco Chronicle*, May 8, 1978, p. 27.
15. "Firm Unable to Guess Toll in LNG Blast," *San Francisco Chronicle*, July 17, 1978, p. 18.
16. A few profits noted in the news:
    11/1/79: Timothy G. Gartner, "Third Quarter: SoCal Earnings Up 110 Percent," *San Francisco Chronicle*, p. 59.
    11/5/79: "Why Profits are Soaring at Major Oil Companies," *San Francisco Chronicle*, p. 62.
    1/26/80: "Record Profit for Exxon—Up 55 Percent in Year," *San Francisco Chronicle*, p. 46.
    2/21/80: "Huge Profits for Oxy Petroleum," *San Francisco Chronicle*, p. 48.
17. *The World Almanac and Book of Facts, 1980*, p. 750.
18. "Exxon Bids $1.165 Billion for Firm," *San Francisco Chronicle*, May 26, 1979, p. 45. The firm: Reliance Electric Company.
19. "Belridge Oil, Shell: Biggest Merger in History is Approved," *San Francisco Chronicle*, December 11, 1979, p. 25.

NOTES TO CHAPTER 4

1. Bradley Graham, "When Yankee Style Unionism Invades the Deep South," *Washington Post*, November 15, 1978.
2. "Faster Rise in Non-Union Wages," *Oakland Tribune*, November 6, 1978, p. 45.
3. "Underpaid Workers," *San Francisco Chronicle*, November 26, 1978, p. A-28.
4. "1 of 4 U.S. Jobs Found Hazardous," *San Francisco Chronicle*, October 3, 1977, p. 5.
5. "Was Jimmy Hoffa Shredded?" *San Francisco Examiner*, September 10, 1978, p. A-2.

NOTES TO CHAPTER 5

1. *San Francisco Chronicle*, May 8, 1979, p. 24.
2. "Cost of Federal Pay Hike: 4 Billion," *U.S. News & World Report*, October 28, 1979, p. 11.

3. Timothy C. Gartner, "Bechtel Hires CIA's Helms as Consultant," *San Francisco Chronicle*, August 18, 1978, p. 1.
4. "Millionaire Who Isn't Ashamed," *San Francisco Chronicle*, June 18, 1978, p. 50.
5. Revenue and Taxation Committee of California Assembly, reported in *Consumer Reports*, September 1979, pp. 546–48.
6. "Property assessments rise sharply," *San Francisco Examiner*, October 2, 1979, p. 10.

NOTES TO CHAPTER 7

1. Milt Moskovitz, "Money Tree: How Dow Makes Borrowing Pay," *San Francisco Chronicle*, June 15, 1979, financial page.
2. Ibid.
3. Pauline G. Hollis, "A Dying Breed: Will There Ever Be Anyone like These Rich Old Men of the West," *San Francisco Chronicle*, August 11, 1979, *People*, p. 11.
4. *New York Times Index*, 1978, p. 1088, col. 3.
5. Robert Reno, "Charity Tax Deductions—How the Rich Get Even Richer," *San Francisco Chronicle*, March 29, 1978, p. BB-2.
6. James Coates, "Marijuana: No. 3 business in America," *San Francisco Examiner*, September 17, 1978, p. 1.

NOTES TO CHAPTER 9

1. Figure of one-third was given by an arms exporter interviewed in a 1979 segment of *60 Minutes*. However, the 1979 *World Almanac* gives the figure of 24–25 percent of our tax dollar for "national defense."
2. First post–World War II recession: 1948. *Encyclopedia Britannica* and *Encyclopedia Americana*.
3. Second post–World War II recession: 1950. Ibid.
4. James McCartney, "President claims otherwise: U.S. arms sales highest ever," *San Francisco Examiner*, July 30, 1978, p. 1.
5. "Defense Bill Passed," *San Francisco Chronicle*, August 15, 1978, p. 6.
6. "Our biggest arms client (Hands Down)," *San Francisco Examiner & Chronicle*, August 27, 1978, p. A-16.
7. James McCartney, op. cit.
8. Steve Rubenstein, "In Livermore the Bomb Is a Part of Life," *San Francisco Chronicle*, September 26, 1977, p. 4.
9. "Use Found for Military Secrets," *San Francisco Chronicle*, November 8, 1977, p. 10.

NOTES TO CHAPTER 10

1. *Moody's Industrial Manual*, 1979, p. 4355.
2. Pauline G. Hollis, "A Dying Breed: Will There Be Anyone like These Rich Old Men of the West?" *San Francisco Chronicle*, August 11, 1979, *People*, p. 11.
3. *Ms.* Magazine, April 1978, pp. 36–40.
4. Jonathan Wolman, "The Demise of the 9–5 Work Week," *San Francisco Sunday Examiner & Chronicle*, August 20, 1978, p. A-12.
5. "From Saddles to Bus Seats," *San Francisco Chronicle*, July 27, 1978, p. 27.
6. Walter Blum, "When Employees Become Owners," *California Living*, December 3, 1978.
7. Milt Moskovitz, "Money Tree: How They Make Cranberries Stretch," *San Francisco Chronicle*, December 12, 1978, p. 8.

NOTES TO CHAPTER 12

1. Ivan Sharpe, "They Don't Take Their Light Bills Lightly in Westwood," *San Francisco Sunday Examiner & Chronicle*, February 19, 1978, p. A-3.

ACKNOWLEDGMENTS

When I think of the many people whose thoughts, ideas, problems, and dreams have found their way into this little book, I know that it is hopeless to even begin to thank them all.

Heartfelt thanks to the many men and women of the working press, and of radio and television who dig away and bring more important matters to light than most of us are able to grasp.

Milt Moskovitz's column, "Money Tree," inspired much of my thinking about conglomerates. Arthur Hoppe, political reporter-turned satirical columnist, who says that he reads the news until he finds something he does not understand, then explains it, gave me a method for looking at facts.

Mike Wallace and his entire staff of *60 Minutes* have lifted the lid off many things that need exposure to light and fresh air.

Closer to home, thanks go to my daughter, Susan, son, David, and my daughter-in-law, Barbara. It was hard work teaching me to get my head out of the clouds and look at the reality around me, but you persevered with my education, though I really do not know what you will think of this product.

Then, too, thanks to my friend Nancy Manahan, who listened, criticized, and encouraged, beginning with page one of draft one; to Suzanne Lippset, who smoothed out many tangles; and most important, to my agent Carol A. Murray, who is not merely an agent, but a super-agent, and who said she would find me the exactly right editor for my *Needle's Eye*, and did. So final heartfelt thanks to my editor, Joyce Johnson, who knows exactly how to do what Shylock could not: slash right and left, and draw not a drop of this writer's blood.